6-8

W9-ATR-893

Pocket card on the back inside cover!

Confessions of a Toe-Hanger
Figleafing Through History
(with Moira Johnston)
Forbidden Frontier
Let X Be Excitement
Once More Upon a Totem
Once Upon a Totem
Raven's Cry
Secret in the Stalalakum Wild
You Have to Draw the Line Somewhere
West With the White Chiefs

SKY MAN
ON THE
TOTEM POLE?

ILLUSTRATED BY DOUGLAS TAIT

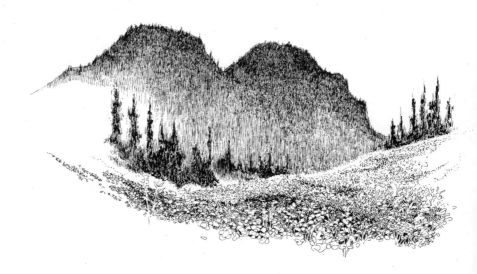

SKY MAN ON THE TOTEM POLE?

Christie Harris

ATHENEUM   1975   NEW YORK

Library of Congress Cataloging in Publication Data

Harris, Christie.
Sky man on the totem pole?

SUMMARY: A retelling of Northwest Indian legends exploring their possible basis in actual events from a space
age perspective.

1. Indians of North America—Northwest, Pacific—
Legends. [1. Indians of North America—Northwest,
Pacific—Legends] I. Tait, Douglas, illus. II. Title.
PZ8.1H22Sk [398.2] 74-19496
ISBN 0-689-30450-X

Text copyright © 1975 by Christie Harris
Illustrations copyright © 1975 by Douglas Tait
All rights reserved
Published simultaneously in Canada by
McClelland & Stewart, Ltd.
Manufactured in the United States of America by
Halliday Lithograph Corporation
West Hanover, Massachussets
Designed by Nora Sheehan
First Edition

To everyone who suspects that legends are fanciful records of history—recountings of actual events that were often misunderstood at the time and then imaginatively interpreted by generations of storytellers.

SKY MAN
ON THE
TOTEM POLE?

before you read the story

L ONG BEFORE THE SPACE AGE, museum men recorded the Northwest Indian legend of Temlaham, which tells of a Man-from-the-Sky whose strange garments caught the sun "like licking tongues of fire."

He carried off an Indian princess, returning her to Earth many years later with six grown-up children. And the noisy return to Earth was made under cover of darkness and a mysterious fog that lingered until the job was done. As the fog lifted, neighbors saw a luminous cloud that emitted lights "like the Northern Lights." Then they saw a "star" moving off.

When fog, cloud, lights, and star were gone, the neighbors were further terrified to see four ready-made houses, each marked by a luminous Sky crest: Sun, Star, Rainbow, and Thunderbird.

But the worst was yet to come; for the Man-from-the-Sky had equipped his family with a weapon that was to be used only in direst need. This was a small box full of mysterious *power*. Some Indian informants called it "the earthquake box," while others claimed that it had caused not a local earthquake but utter annihilation of the thing it was used against.

Because the report of the event had been passed down from generation to generation of people owning the Sky crests, the Indians who told the story firmly believed in their own descent from a Man-from-the-Sky. Only the coming of the white man made it begin to seem an embarrassing myth to them.

Now, however, in a time of startling Space Age discoveries, who can be sure that a Man-from-the-Sky did not land on Earth near a Northwest Indian village? Complete with plastic clothes, ray gun, vapor screen, prefabricated houses and luminous paint.

The Indians of the Pacific Northwest recorded legendary events in symbols we see on their totem poles: Eagle, Raven, Wolf, Killer Whale, Frog, Thunderbird . . . and who can be sure that Thunderbird didn't originate as the symbol for a spaceman zooming into the mountains on a rocket belt?

The Thunderbird may possibly be explained in this flesh-and-blood way. But who is to say that some of the other supernatural beings weren't quite as real *without* being flesh and blood? For instance, the

4

spirit people of the forest.

After recent discoveries in the plant world, there's a new interest in the primitive belief in nature spirits. Scientists are discovering that there is indeed a conscious energy animating trees and grasses; and to their solids, liquids, and gases, they're having to add a "fourth state of matter"—an invisible *something* that defies accepted physical laws of their science books. Could their "fourth state of matter" be the "mystic realms" of the old storytellers? Are there indeed spirits in the forest and mountains, in the seas and rivers? Is there even an actual, mystical power in the old totem pole?

The totem pole carries its legendary characters all on one side; for tradition decrees that there is no other side to the totem pole. But need the modern storyteller be as restricted as the traditional Indian story illustrator?

Mightn't the storyteller be allowed to make a few informed guesses about what may belong on the *other side* of the old legend of Temlaham?

one

It was in the time of very long ago. And a day was dawning.

A raven called from the top of a totem pole. Other ravens answered from the dark forest that rose behind the arc of cedar houses. Gulls wheeled and screamed above the beach. The sea mist began to stir. And along the shore, the canoes emerged, silent as ghost ships behind their towering emblems.

In the biggest of the houses a young man rose from his sleeping platform. Hushed as a ghost, he glided through the gloom of the big, windowless house, pausing only to narrow his eyes over the filthy sleeping form sprawled by the ashes of the fire. Then, si-

6

lent as an owl, he slipped out of the house and ran into the forest.

As he followed the trail that ran close to the beach, sea mists hovered around him like the ghosts of his ancestors. But Adinak moved swiftly through them until he came out on a rocky point. And there he stood, scowling, while the shrouded sea swells broke on the dark rock below him.

Was Say-ok, his youngest brother, possessed by an evil spirit? The sudden thought widened his eyes with alarm. But what else could explain the boy's filth and insolence? What else could lure him away from the proper ways? What else could keep him out of the house, night after night, until nearly dawn?

Adinak's mouth tightened with distaste for the slovenly hulk sprawled by the ashes of the fire. Where was Say-ok's respect for his place in the tribe? How could he so dishonor the name that had been worn by generations of noble ancestors? No wonder the people refused to call him Say-ok. No wonder they dubbed him Prince Filthy. But what a humiliation to his uncle, the Eagle Chief, his guardian by the custom of the northern people! Adinak flushed with the shame of his youngest brother.

Suddenly he shivered. But it was not from the sea wind. It was a sudden foreboding that chilled the young man who was heir to the Eagle Chief by the tribe's matriarchal laws of succession. Something was going to happen.

He felt it in the trees of the crowding forest. They knew that something was going to happen. He pressed himself close to the trunk of a giant cedar;

but the flow of power was less than on other days. The spirits of the Earth were aware of something. Frightened by something.

Adinak dived into the cold, shrouded sea to cleanse himself for better contact with the spirit world. And when he came out, he rubbed his skin with cedar boughs, pulling each branch down to let its spirit power flow into his body, then letting it spring back to fling his prayer upward into its mighty Being. But the usual rush of well-being failed him. Something was going to happen. The invisible people of the forest knew it was going to happen. And they were shrinking back in fear.

Had an evil spirit taken possession of Say-ok? The way an evil spirit sometimes took possession of a shaman, turning him from a good medicine man into a sorcerer who killed with a dreadful magic? Terrible things could happen when an evil spirit entered into a human, replacing his true spirit Self.

Only special power could deal with possession by an evil spirit. And special power was bestowed on humans only when they had become worthy of it.

He wished he had trained as a shaman. He wished he had suffered the years of physical hardships and fasts and wanderings alone in the wilderness. Then his spirit Self would have been so pure that it could have broken free of the clutches of his body and traveled to the faraway mystic realms where the great Spirits could have given him mighty power, and a spirit vision for his people.

Adinak caught his breath at a sudden thought. "Spirit vision!"

Once, in the days of long before, a shaman had been given the vision of Temlaham, the Promised Land. And for years the tribe had followed the vision . . . wandering . . . hunting . . . camping . . . paddling . . . out of their Old World into this stormy New World. But they had wearied of migration, of never building proper shelters against the biting gales and the lashing rainstorms. And at last, abandoning the sacred vision, they had built their great houses.

"Someday soon we'll take up the quest again," they had promised one another.

But the spirit vision had gradually faded away in the blazing warmth of their lodge fires. And now they no longer said, "Someday . . ." Now they strove just to live well off the bounty of the sea and the forest.

What if this was angering the great Spirits who had given them the vision of Temlaham? What if the great Spirits were going to punish the people who had not proved worthy?

Adinak shuddered again with that terrible sense of foreboding.

Something *was* going to happen. The invisible people of the forest knew it was going to happen.

A light in the sky caught his attention. A star! But . . . That couldn't be. Now? When all the stars of the night had faded?

But it was a star. And it was MOVING. Moving across the sky. Across and down.

Toward the mystic realms?

He sank to the earth, trembling. This was a mighty sign. And the spirits around him told him it was a *bad* sign. Something was going to happen.

Tribal memory flooded him with fear. For the old stories told of destruction that had come from the sky, once in the days of very long ago. Raining hot stones. Moving mountains. And washing away villages with great waves from the sea.

Something was going to happen.

two

S OMETHING WAS GOING TO HAPPEN.
Alien forces were moving toward the planet.

The threat was out there in the cold black silence of space. It was out there beyond the "star" that had alarmed Adinak.

The "star" was the spaceship *Colonizer*. It was now under emergency orders from its home planet, Tlu. Tlu had an Earth colony far south of the totem poles. The ship had been on its way home from the colony when it had received a signal from Tlu. *Comet on collision vector with planet Earth. Evacuate data banks and colonists.* The *Colonizer* had reversed course. It was nearing Earth again.

Its captain, Laetl, frowned as he looked ahead. But his frown was not for what would happen to Earth. His frown was for the weird thing that had happened to him.

It had happened just before the signal had come from Tlu. He had seen a spirit Being. Yet he could not have seen a spirit Being. So it had been an hallucination. His brain had malfunctioned again.

"Spirits are not an acceptable fact," he muttered to himself. "Yet—" Yet hallucinations were not an acceptable fact either to a career man in Space Service. He shook his head to clear it. He turned his attention to the planet before him.

"Earth." He had taken on the tree there. He was to transport it to Tlu for the plant specialists.

No. He would not think about the small tree. That tree spirit had been an hallucination. But it was strange that it had come immediately before the signal from Tlu. As if it had known the message was on its way.

He had been checking on the Earth plants in his cargo. Suddenly he had sensed a presence. He had turned to see who it was, and all he had seen was a luminous mist rising from the tree. The mist had concentrated itself into a small, sparkling, hominoid form. It had thrust out its hand in a STOP! signal.

At that moment the crewman had come in with the message from Tlu. And when Laetl could turn to look again, the Being had vanished. The tree was as it had always been, green and still in the simulated sunlight.

Laetl shook his head again. He switched his

13

thoughts to the comet.

There had been further word about the comet. It was not huge like the comet that had devastated Earth in an earlier accident. But its course was destructive. Some other cosmic body might pull it off orbit again. Otherwise it would hit Earth. And there were important data banks as well as important people on Earth at the moment.

"Earth!" As he spoke the word aloud, Laetl's voice held an emotion unworthy of a career man in Space Service. Earth had an insidious effect on a man. Its fresh green wildernesses were a contrast to Tlu's stark cities laced together by air and land transport. The green was restful to space-weary eyes. And Earth's birds reached ancient, almost forgotten data in the Tlu memory bank. They found traces of the primitive Tluman.

Laetl switched his mind back to the comet. Tlu's astrono-puters calculated that it would crash into Earth near the equator. It would hit like an atomic blast. It would topple trees for a hundred miles out. It would send shock waves through the ocean.

The *Colonizer* would evacuate Tlumen. The local natives would perish.

Yet a few would survive. Against probabilities, they always did. Earth had been devastated by worse cosmic accidents. Always people had survived to tell about it. Every contacted tribe had its tales of former ages that had ended in fire or flood, in tempest or earthquake. And the tribes always thought that they had brought on the catastrophe. Their tales were full of small, wicked deeds that had brought on a flood,

an earthquake, or a volcanic eruption. Always someone had been breaking the rules. Always someone
had been offending the "spirits" of the mountains or
sea or sky. The Earth Superstitions data bank was
full of the weird logic of the primitive mind.

Now, the comet would crash near the colony. Later,
the survivors there would wrack their memories.
They would discover what bad thing someone had
done to offend the Spirits-of-the-Sky. Or to offend
the departed Gods-from-the-Sky.

Laetl dismissed Gods with an amused smile. The
natives knew nothing of advanced technology. So
they equated technology with magic. They thought
the colonists were supernatural Beings-from-the-Sky.
"Sons of the Sun," they called the fair-haired Tlumen.
Even he, Laetl, was a "God" with magical powers to
help or harm them.

"Gods," he muttered. "But . . . spirits?"

Suddenly his eyes widened with a shocking idea.
What if spirits were a FACT? What if they were a fact
not yet fed into Tluan computers?

Tlumen scoffed at Earthmen's "spirits." Yet there
were mysteries their own computers could cope with
only as "hallucinations." His ice blue eyes hardened.
He remembered an "hallucination." Once he had
stayed too long at one instrument. And he had
glimpsed strange little men. He had watched misty
miniatures until they had dissipated, like mists. The
psycho-puters had diagnosed them as "hallucinations," as "perceptual aberrations due to stress factors." They had computed that for a few minutes his
brain had malfunctioned.

His disciplined mind had accepted that. But now, suddenly, he challenged the diagnosis. What if the diagnosis had been computed from insufficient data? What if the data bank had lacked an entire set of facts? What if certain facts had not yet been discovered? After all, any computer was a prisoner of its program. It was not free to offer new facts.

His mind raced, tracking the startling idea. Perhaps, just perhaps, his brain had not malfunctioned that time. Perhaps he actually had glimpsed beings from a higher frequency of matter. Perhaps he really had seen people from another dimension of life.

Laetl's logical mind raced on. Earthmen accepted a spirit world. And since they lived close to nature, there was the probability that they sensed a cosmic fact the "Gods" of Tlu had been too technically arrogant, too mechanistic minded to consider. The natives near the colony were corn planters. They invoked the spirits of the corn. They invoked the spirits of the rain. And they were deathly serious about it. So what if it were not all superstitious nonsense?

Added to that, there was the probability that the data that had been fed into Tlumen all their lives simply did not equip them to compute a spirit world.

So! What if his brain had not malfunctioned that time?

Or. An equally shocking idea gripped him. What if his brain were malfunctioning again? Now. What if he were losing his grip on reality? It happened to many Tlumen. And such men were swiftly dealt with.

"Spirits?" Laetl challenged himself. He was unsure, anxious.

A hovering crewman coughed respectfully to catch his captain's attention. Then he boomed out his question to cover the fact that he had caught the Ship Master mumbling to himself, again. "What do you compute will happen, Ship Master?"

"To Earth?" With computer efficiency, Laetl's mind sorted through the facts. The previous comet had merely brushed the planet. Yet it had moved mountains. It had submerged large lands. It had rained boulders. It had lifted seas to mountainous heights. Then the released seas had crashed down on the lands. And the devastated planet had been left unstable. It had been left subject to earthquakes and volcanic eruptions.

But those facts were instantly set against the fact that this comet was not a big one. "The devastation will be local."

He was still gripped by his shocking idea. He turned sharp eyes on the crewman. He considered the desirability of slipping a new probability into the logical minds of his crew. "Tur, have you ever glimpsed a spirit Being?"

"Spirit Being?" The crewman's widened eyes betrayed his thoughts. The Ship Master had hallucinated once when he was new to Space Service; that once was acceptable. But now the Ship Master had hallucinated again. That could deeply disturb his crew.

"You have heard of spirits?" Laetl prodded him.

"I have heard of spirits, Ship Master. But—" But spirits were "seen" only by witch doctors. Spirits were "seen" by wild-eyed savages who had worked themselves up into a frenzy with drums and dancing, until they saw things that were not there. "But how could I see spirits, Ship Master?"

"You could see them if they were a fact. Earthmen see spirits."

"Earthmen." Tur's tone placed Earthmen very low in the category of human beings. Earthmen had not risen far above the hairy primates. They clung to one another like animal packs. They suckled their young like apes. They identified with beasts. They talked to them as brothers.

"Spirits could be a fact," Laetl coldly pointed out. "We have refused to seriously research 'superstitious nonsense.' So there is the possibility that we have left gaps in our information. There is the possibility that primitives key their senses up to a higher frequency through drums and dances. Through this they enable themselves to tune in on matter that vibrates with a higher frequency. A higher frequency than we have computed."

"Of course, Ship Master." Tur's anxious eyes said there was yet another possibility: the Captain was cracking up under the stresses of command. "Of course, Ship Master," he repeated. Then he backed off very, very respectfully, and very fast. Tur had things to tell his shipmates.

Laetl frowned after him. "There is logic in it," he assured himself. Tlumen had arrogant control of their world. But they had not necessarily reached the apogee of knowledge. There could be new input in their data banks. There were strange concepts in that Earth Superstitions data bank. He would explore them on

the voyage home.

Then Laetl switched his mind back to his mission. A comet was on a collision vector with planet Earth. The *Colonizer* was to evacuate data banks and colonists.

Local Earthmen would perish. Others all along that coastline might be almost wiped out by shock waves. And their survivors would think it was punishment from the spirit world.

three

I T WAS MANY MORNINGS LATER, a clear morning after a week of wild rainstorms.

A raven called from the top of a totem pole. And other ravens answered from the dark forest that rose behind the arc of cedar houses. Gulls wheeled and screamed above the canoes that waited, silent and ready, behind their towering totems: Eagle, Raven, Wolf, and Bear.

Soon young crews were moving toward the canoes, as graceful and lively and naked as the seabirds. For though the water was still too rough for the sea hunt, it was a good sea for training.

Sliding his gaze over his young Eagles, Adinak's

dark eyes warmed with affection for two of his brothers, already superb seamen. Then he flushed with shame as he caught sight of his youngest brother. As dirty as ever, Say-ok was lolling against a drift stump on the beach, insolently eyeing the crew he should have been going out with. *Was* he possessed by an evil spirit?

Turning quickly to banish that persisting sense of foreboding, Adinak scanned the sea and the sky. Already the morning gave promise of one of those glorious blue-and-white days when the world seemed full of blue mountains with white snow peaks, blue sea with white surf, and blue sky with white clouds and the white flash of sea gulls.

"Ready?" he asked his Eagles.

They were ready and eager to be out on the water again. For, confined as they were to the beach by the jungle of rain forest and the crowding mountains, they knew the sea as their hunting ground and their playground. The sea was their freedom.

Four canoes moved off from the village. And as each totem-carved prow breasted the wind and the sea, it seemed one with the young paddlers who rhythmically bent backs tattooed with a matching totem. Each craft seemed a supernatural being, moving powerfully through the northern ocean. And a thrill of pride swept through the watching families.

Seeming disdainful of paddlers and watchers alike, Say-ok still lolled against the drift stump. If *his* body was tattooed, the crest was lost under a filth of ashes. Only his long hair and his ear ornaments showed that he was not a slave, but a noble.

There was little respect, though, in the glances tossed his way by passing girls and women. Some held their noses. Others bent their necks and muttered, "Prince Filthy" with mock ceremony.

He waved off their contempt. He smiled; and the smile hid his humiliation, his fury.

His fury was for his brothers, out there in the Eagle canoe. Everything they did, they did superbly, as princes should. And he hated them. Handsome, strong, courageous, courteous and skilled, *they* were a credit to the Eagles. Their feet never slipped on a wet rock. Their paddles never twisted in their firm hands. And he hated them. As he hated the villagers who mocked him. But he would show them. All of them. Let them laugh! For his own laugh was coming.

A woman in a shredded cedar-bark robe glided toward him. "Why didn't you go out in the training canoe?" she demanded of him. Her voice was wistful as well as angry.

"Who wants me?" Say-ok held his own nose the way the passing girls had held theirs.

"Yes. Who?" she agreed. "Since you loll about in filth. Why don't you bathe like the other boys? Why don't you chew devil's club for power? Why don't you do something?"

"I may, Aunt," he answered lazily, as if he didn't much care. "Who knows? I may." Yet inside he felt a hint of triumph. She would see. They all would.

"Uch!" She whirled away from him, blinking back tears of frustration. And he knew what she was thinking. A dirty, lazy, good-for-nothing youth shamed his whole family. And especially he shamed his Chief, the uncle responsible for making him a credit to the Eagles. He knew he angered the Chief so fiercely that she, the Chief's wife, was hard put to defend him.

When the canoes were gone and the people had drifted away, Say-ok slouched off into the forest and lay down on a sheltered bank of moss. Before going to sleep, he chewed purposefully at a piece of devil's club.

It was late in the day before he stirred. First he glanced furtively around and leaned his ear this way and that. Then he leaped to his feet, grim with purpose.

Following animal trails, skirting beaches, clambering over rocks, crashing through underbrush, and following streams, he ran a long, long, long way. And as though daring the invisible people of the forest to make things worse for him than they already were, he never paused to spare a branch or a small clump of bushes. When he fell from a decaying log, he kicked at the deep mosses that had cushioned his fall.

The forest held its silence. Owls swooped, silent as ghosts, through the gloom of the coming night. Then the high, eerie cry of a wolf broke the quiet. And other wolves answered from deep in the forest.

At last Say-ok reached his training place, a rocky point jutting out into the sea. Here, strong young evergreens were growing at the edge of the forest. And as if challenging the tree spirits, he grasped one. With an effort that made the veins stand out in his neck, he twisted it down to its very roots. Then he untwisted it and twisted another tree. And yet another, as he did every night.

The trees, as though faint with fear of the savage youth, were as still as death in the shadowed dark.

Too full of his own fury to sense the alarm of the spirit world around him, or to notice the sky, the fierce youth tested his strength by tearing branches of bigger trees right out of their sockets. His eyes glittered with a defiance that was almost maniacal glee. As if he were indeed possessed by an evil spirit.

Then he kindled a fire on a secreted pile of stones and fed it thick chunks of bark from a secret store. He was looking about for more fuel when he rounded a high rock, and caught his breath. A fierce light flamed and flared on the mountain skyline to the south. It was like a fantastic wolf's head trailing a serpent's body. "A Sky Monster!" A hideously beautiful Sky Monster! Had it been there before? Heavy overcast and rainstorms had hidden the sky from him for weeks.

Trembling with fright, he slunk back behind the rock, where it couldn't see him. "A Sky Monster!" And the others, asleep in their houses, knew nothing about it. Only HE knew. A supernatural Sky Wolf! And the wolves of the forest were crying out to it. On impulse, he cried out with the wolves.

Then it struck him. Wolf! The Wolf was the hunter's sign. And only HE had been given the sign. Only HE would be spectacularly successful in the coming sea hunt. He dared out from his hiding place to face the Sky Wolf. To hold his arms up to it. To feel its power flowing into his body. Then with fierce confidence he raced back to his final burst of training.

Leaving the stones to heat in the burning bark, he

24

twisted one last tree down to its very roots. Then he dived into the sea; and for a brief time he swam in its numbing waters.

The tide was out. And the exposed rocks were slippery with wet seaweed. Yet, when he came out, he leaped from rock to rock, keeping his balance. Then he dived into the sea again. He dived and swam and leaped until it seemed he must perish on the cruel rocks or else in the crueler sea.

When he came out to stay, Say-ok flayed his flesh with green boughs he had wrenched from the trees. "A Sky Monster!" he kept muttering. And his eyes kept turning toward the towering rocks that hid it from him.

Coals of bark smoldered now among the stones; and the stones were hot. So he covered them with a thick mat of wet moss and lay down in the steam, under a cedar-bark mat he had also secreted.

When at last he got up, he dived one more time into the sea. Then he straightened himself with pride, a pride the villagers would never have suspected. Standing on a moonlit rock, holding his arms up and out in prayer, he faced the rocks that hid the Sky Monster from an unsuspecting village. He felt its POWER flowing into him. And he cried out again like a wolf.

"Now I am ready," he announced. And, as if in answer, a wolf sent his high, eerie call out of the timbered mountains.

Purposefully he smudged his gleaming wet skin with ashes. Then he glided the long, long, long way back to the village, where he slunk into sleeping Eagle House. And like the lazy, good-for-nothing youth they all thought him, he lay down by the ashes of the dead fire.

Tomorrow Prince Filthy would show them. All of them! And especially his handsome, strong, courageous, courteous, skilled, hated brothers.

four

THE RAVENS CALLED. And the village stirred with a special excitement.

"Today we hunt the sea lions," the Eagle Chief told his people. "And all the young men who are ready will go with us."

After all the stormy weather, the village was in need of meat.

Say-ok saw his brothers trot toward the readied canoes. Their quick eyes checked on ropes and clubs, spears and bladder floats. Already skilled sea hunters, they stood proud and ready, sure of their place in the day's hunt. And, as if his heart were not throbbing fiercely, he sauntered over to join them.

The instant consternation of the people was like the first rumblings of thunder. But he showed no concern. He hid his secret as the timbered mountains had hidden the Sky Monster from them.

The Chief frowned. "Only the powerful may go to the sea lions' island," he called out, as though speaking to everybody. The way was rough, he reminded them. Sea lions were scarce this year; and their island was treacherously slippery. Only the need for meat sent the hunters at this time to the perilous task. "This is work for strong arms and sure feet."

Say-ok could feel his Chief's frown. But he stood his ground, hugging his terrible secret to him. He shifted his weight lazily from one foot to the other and indolently chewed on nothing to hide his surging defiance.

His uncle's eyes flashed. But his aunt's tug at her husband's robe reminded the Chief that the boy must not be shamed further if he were ever to become a credit to the Eagles.

Say-ok had counted on that. But he seemed not to notice.

"Let him go!" a woman called out. "Prince Filthy needs a good wash."

"True," another agreed in a loud voice, "but do the whales deserve such a fouling?"

Yet others held their noses, defiantly. Their deep, ingrained fear of offending the ocean spirits and the Great Sea Lion Spirit made them bold to speak out, even against the Chief's nephew, his fourth-in-line heir.

Say-ok saw that his uncle's eyes were narrowed

thoughtfully; his gaze was sliding over the careless-seeming body of his youngest nephew. Penetrating its secret?

"Say-ok will go with us!" the Chief commanded.

Sea hunters closed their lips tight over unspoken protests. Their Chief had spoken.

"Let him sleep on the journey!" a still-defiant woman called out, her voice full of sarcasm. "Then he will be ready to leap out first."

As if completely unconcerned by the scorn, Say-ok got into one of the two Eagle canoes and relaxed. He yawned, and pretended to be sleepy. But he was sharply aware of the alarmed glances exchanged by the sea hunters. Such insolence as his, they were thinking, would offend the sea spirits and the Great Sea Lion Spirit. They knew calamity would happen.

But the Chief had spoken.

The sea seemed rougher than usual. But the crews had been born to a wild sea. They made vigorously for the island.

The sea lions' island was out in the open ocean, beyond the fringe of islands. Great swells broke on it. And its rocks were slippery.

As they neared it, the roar of the beasts reached them. The paddlers darted keen glances at the awesome animals. Some gallumphed their glossy bodies over the rocks to the water's edge to catch a giant wave and let it launch them into the deep, deep cold sea. Others swam toward the island and let the swells lift them back onto the rocks. They were lords of this wild world.

Keenly aware of their own intrusion into another's

world, the paddlers drew warily close.

The Chief stood ready to leap. He waited until a swell lifted him level with the rocks. Then he jumped. And seizing a small sea lion by the tail, he smashed its head against a rock. Then he tackled a bigger one. Sitting astride its tail, he prepared for the deadly blow. But the enraged beast threw him up into the air, smashing him—fatally—against the rocks.

The crews gasped in horror. Fear filled their dark eyes. But, before they could lose heart, Adinak, captaining the other canoe, readied himself for the leap. The people needed meat; and a noble's first duty was to the people. He waited for the swell to lift him up to the rocks. Then he jumped. But his foot slipped on the treacherous rocks, and he fell, cruelly hurt by the rocks and then smashed by the pounding sea. He sank from sight and was carried away by the undertow.

Now the men were tense. The ocean spirits and the Great Sea Lion Spirit were deeply offended. It would be a calamitous day. And they blamed Say-ok. They were sure he had neglected to perform the prehunt rites that appeased the spirits.

Say-ok knew what they were thinking. He felt the angry eyes on him. And in return, he glared his defiance. This was not his doing. The Sky Monster was in command. So he faced the angry eyes in grim silence.

Before fury could burst out among the crews, the second of the Chief's nephews stood up, gracefully balancing his weight against the swells. Hiding his grief under ceremony, he took abalone pearl ornaments out of a small pouch and offered them to the sea spirits. Next he took out tufts of white eagle down and wafted them reverently toward the sea lions. Then, catching the crest of the next swell, he leaped toward the island.

But his fate was like his brother's. His broken body, too, went down into the cold depths of the unforgiving sea.

When the same thing happened to the third brother, both crews trembled with fear. The spirits had indeed been offended. And the hunt must be abandoned, in spite of the need for meat.

Say-ok felt the decision coming. He felt his long-planned triumph slipping away from him, like a salmon that had been almost within his grasp. And with the cry of a wolf he leaped to his feet. The Sky

Monster was with him, giving him the power he needed. Balancing his weight against the heaving sea, he too took things out of a small pouch. He flung them into the sea. Then he stood ready to leap.

Men stared at him, stunned.

"Take the canoe in close!" he ordered.

Eyes narrowed. Mouths clamped shut over a mounting fury. Prince Filthy was the dead Chief's heir now. But the tribe would never confirm him as Chief. There was no need to obey him.

"Let him go!" a paddler burst out. "The tribe is well rid of him. And maybe the offended spirits will accept his death as atonement for his sins against them."

"Take the canoe in close!" Say-ok's voice carried the command of a long line of sea hunting chiefs.

The canoe surged in with the next swell. And he leaped out onto the treacherous rocks.

His feet did not slip.

But now there was no triumph in the feat. For, suddenly, the fury left him, like an evil spirit that had done its work. And it left his true spirit Self filled with grief for his uncle's death and with guilt for his brothers' deaths. His evil spirit had killed them. His hatred had drowned them just as surely as a sorcerer's spite killed people.

There was no triumph in the feat. There was only dark desperation in the swift, sure blows-to-the-head that killed two small sea lions.

He made for the beast that had killed his uncle. And with all his fierce tree-twisting strength and with all the fury of his guilt, he killed it and dragged it to

33

where the depleted crews readied themselves to take on the carcasses.

As they worked in the heaving sea, the men kept glancing at Prince Filthy and there was a new terror in their thoughts. They had ridiculed him often. And who knew? Who knew where he had found this sudden monstrous strength? Who knew if a supernatural Being—a dread *naq noq*—animated him now? And would retaliate against them for their scorn.

Say-ok knew what was going to happen. And, staggered now by a terrible guilt for the day's tragedies, he was fiercely glad it was going to happen. His overpowering hatred had drowned his brothers, the way the evil power of a sorcerer killed people. And only by drowning, too, could he appease their ghosts. He had offended the spirits, too. He had performed the prehunt rites; but he had performed them fiercely, without proper reverence. The spirits, too, would be appeased only by his drowning.

He was the only living heir. But he was not worthy to be Chief. The people would never accept him when he made the claim his birth would force him to make. And their rejection of his claim to Chiefhood would be the final humiliation in a life of humiliation.

Only HE had seen the Sky Monster because the sign *had* been for him. But it had not been the promise of the Hunter. It had been the sign of the evil that had possessed him.

He knew what was going to happen. And grimly he let it happen. When the last carcass was secured, the paddlers plied their blades in flight. Instead of waiting for the next swell to lift them to the rocks to take off their Chief's body and the now-fearsome Prince Filthy, they fled for home.

As if chased by an evil spirit, they sprinted for the village.

Unmoving as a rock, Say-ok watched them go.

five

"WHERE IS THE CHIEF?" his widow demanded when they had touched the beach. "And where are his four nephews?"

When the men had tumbled out their story, she drew herself up. "Go back to the island!" she commanded. "Bring back the Chief's body! And bring back his living heir!"

The men cowered back. Though ashamed now of their flight from the island of death, they were still in terror of the youth they had left there.

"They are too weary for such a trip," an old sea hunter noted. "I will go with fresh paddlers." And having saved face for his terrified clansmen, he quickly selected a crew.

Now the sea was even rougher than before. But these men had spent their lives on it. So they made vigorously for the island. The shame of leaving their Chief's body where it was spurred them on, in spite of the roar of the beasts.

They neared the island. Drew skillfully close. A man stood ready to leap. He waited until the next swell lifted him level with the rocks. Then he jumped.

With success!

A sigh of relief swept the tense crew. The spirits had been appeased. At last the spirits had been appeased.

But where was Prince Filthy?

Another man joined the first on the rocks, while the paddlers kept the canoe safe from the pounding sea and the cruel rocks. Respectfully they moved their Chief's body to the canoe.

But where was his living heir?

Fear deepened in the eyes of the wary crew. And there was haste in their arms as they paddled home. What had happened to the prince they had ridiculed? Had he indeed been a supernatural Being sent to test them? And would some further calamity now come to the village in retaliation?

All night the wailing of the people for their Chief and his heirs carried out on the winds that howled around Eagle House. Drums beat. Ghostly cedar bugles sounded. And shamans shook their rattles as they danced their frenzied dances about the lodge fire.

Suddenly, the old Eagle shaman leaped away from

the other dancers and stood still as a tree, as though listening intently to something the others could not hear. Under the ring of grizzly bear claws that crowned his long straggle of gray hair, his eyes glittered and shifted, as though watching something the others could not see.

The drums quieted. The ghostly cedar bugles ceased. The other shamans slowed their steps and muffled their rattles. All eyes turned on the alert, silent figure of the old man.

"There is a cave high in the rocks," he whispered hoarsely.

The people nodded, numbly. There was a cave on the towering rocky point, south of the village.

"Bring food and sleeping robes," he said, gliding silently toward the doorway.

Trembling now with fear of some new calamity, people grabbed up food and robes and torches and little children. They streamed out into the predawn.

What had the shaman seen in the spirit world? What had the spirits told him?

Scrambling over rocks, they rounded the base of a towering rock cliff, and saw the Sky Monster. A terrible, beautiful Wolf's head flamed and flared above the mountain skyline.

"A Sky Wolf!" people gasped, sinking to the rocks in terror. "A Sky Wolf with a serpent's body!"

"Perhaps it—" But no one dared to say what everyone was thinking: that perhaps this was the monstrous Being who had used the body of Prince Filthy; that perhaps this was the hideous *naq noq* who would retaliate against them.

Stumbling and scrambling in the dark shadows, they fled on to the cave, where they couldn't see the Sky Monster. And there, families huddled together. Mothers clutched their children to them. For who knew what would happen?

Engulfed now in tribal memory of the cataclysm that had come from the Sky, once, in the days of very long ago, they waited for the mountains to move; they waited for the sea to inundate them.

All day they waited, and all through the next dark night. And no one dared to go out, except the shaman.

Then the raven cried, bringing another day.

"The Sky Monster has gone," the old shaman told them.

"Gone?" The voices held less terror. "So we can go home now?"

"Not yet," the shaman answered. His ears still listened to what the others could not hear. And under his long straggle of gray hair, his eyes still glittered and shifted, as though watching something the others could not see.

So the people waited . . . and waited . . .

Then the sea came, swirling around the rocks below them. It hurled drift logs at the cliffs and raced on toward the village.

When at last it flooded back again, it carried drift logs, uprooted trees, cedar planks, and smashed canoes.

The families huddled together, wide-eyed and trembling.

six

AT LAST THE PEOPLE VENTURED OUT into the ruins of their village. Canoes were gone. Great cedar houses were smashed. Proud crest poles were broken, aslant, fallen. And cherished regalia, now wet and bedraggled, spilled out of boxes wedged under fallen timbers.

"What did we do?" a very old woman wailed, rocking herself back and forth on a rock.

"We know what we did," her husband answered her, gently. "We ridiculed a youth who was really a *naq noq.*"

"We know what we did," her son echoed. "But what must we do now?"

"I will find out," the old Eagle shaman said. "Tonight I will find out."

Still wild-eyed, still in touch with the spirit world, he stood apart from the people in his intense listening way. And while they sorted through the debris of their homes, he vanished into the gloomy world, silent as an owl.

By the time he returned, shelters had been organized. But the people had scrambled back up to the cave in fear of what the dark night might bring. They had a fire blazing in the cave. They had sacred herbs dried out, ready to waft powerful smoke around him.

All eyes turned on him as he leaped into the cave.

"Tonight I will find out," he said, taking a steaming herbal drink from one of his wives.

When he had drunk it, he settled the crown of grizzly bear claws over his long straggle of gray hair. He secured the apron that clattered with a fringe of birds' beaks. Then, as sticks began to drum against the rocks of the cave, he chanted a wild song, shaking his medicine rattle and sweeping the air with the white tail of an eagle.

Pressing back against the cave walls, people watched him begin his dance. And many fixed their fearful gazes on the fantastic dancing of his shadow self, flung from his body by the bright flames. As the beat quickened, as the dance grew more frenzied, they took over the chant. And their voices rose shriller and shriller, while the sticks beat faster and faster, and the dance grew more and more frenzied.

Then, suddenly, the shaman stopped. Wild-eyed and exhausted, he flung himself down on the tattered

old wolfskin his wives had readied for him. And he lay there as though dead.

The watchers caught their breaths. Then they took up the beating and chanting again, softly, so as not to disturb him. For now the shaman's spirit Self was leaving his body to make the perilous journey into the other world, the world of ghosts and spirits and supernatural beings. It was always a fearsome time. For who knew how terrible were the powers he might have to confront out there? And who knew what word he might bring back?

The fire died down. The gloom of the cave deepened. The singing hushed. Eyes peered through the gloom to watch the shaman as the people waited . . . and waited . . . and waited . . .

Men almost held their breaths, for silence, as they fed the dying fire. And the people waited . . .

Did his eyelids flutter?

The singing rose again, softly, to call his soul back to his waiting body. And the sticks quickened.

The shaman stirred.

Helpers glided to him while the awed watchers stood still as stone. What word would he bring back from the world of ghosts and spirits? What terrible thing might be demanded of the tribe that had deeply offended the other world?

The shaman sat up, gray and haggard. But his eyes glinted.

"My soul left my body," he told the people. "It traveled toward the sunrise. To Temlaham."

"Temlaham?" They scarcely whispered the old, almost forgotten name of the Promised Land.

"Temlaham!" they said again, more happily. There was only good in Temlaham.

"Temlaham is still waiting." And the hoarse old voice began to tell of the land he had seen—a land where the mountains watched over flower-filled meadows, mountains where the goats leaped and the eagles circled. He told of rivers teeming with salmon. Of banks thick with berries. "Temlaham is still waiting," he said again.

Hope brightened their faces and voices as the people turned to one another. Their ancestors had had a vision of Temlaham, back in the days of very long ago. They had followed the dream through storm and ice until they had wearied of the long migration and had built the first houses of this village.

"We'll move on," the Chiefs said. And people echoed them on all sides.

"Perhaps that's what we did wrong," a few suggested. "Ending the migration before we had found the Promised Land."

"That could have angered the spirit world," others agreed. But now, after all these generations, a new migration was starting, with a new vision of Temlaham. And this time the tribe would not falter on the way. "This time we will find Temlaham."

Weary from the day's work and the night's excitement, they settled down to sleep. But many were restless. "Temlaham is still waiting," they kept whispering to one another, as if trying to believe such good news from the other world.

They could hardly wait for morning to start travel preparations. Canoes would have to be chipped and burned out of fallen timbers. Food would have to be readied. Regalia that was too ancient and sacred to be abandoned would have to be refurbished. An Eagle Chief would have to be chosen, and properly validated. For the tribe would move as it had always moved, with dignity befitting a people bound for the Promised Land.

Then, suddenly, it was morning. A raven called from a rock near the cave. Other ravens answered from the shattered forest. Sea gulls wheeled and screamed above the beach, calling people to a busy day.

Temlaham was waiting.

"Where is it waiting?" children asked their elders.

"Toward the sunrise."

That was the only direction their ancestors had had when they had left their Old World, back in the days of very long ago. But snow and ice and impassable, timbered mountains had turned them from the sunrise and sent them south along the wild coast until they had wearied.

"But we'll not weary," they assured one another. They would find Temlaham and live forever near the mountains where the goats leaped and the eagles circled, near the rivers that teemed with salmon.

They would forget what had happened here.

No. They would not forget. And they would not let their children or their children's children forget the powers that were OUT THERE, ready to punish an erring people.

The Sky Monster had had a wolf's head, they reminded one another, as well as a serpent's body; and

45

the wolf was the hunter's sign. Perhaps it had meant that they should leave the coast and become great goat hunters.

The shattered village took on new life. Men chipped at canoes and fished from a rocky headland. Women dug clams and smoked their husbands' fish catches. Children fetched and carried. And bird beaks clattered as shamans invoked friendly spirits of sea, air, and mountains.

People sighed over carved house posts that would have to be abandoned. But they would carve better ones in Temlaham. They approved canoes not rubbed to a polish nor handsomely decorated. They would make finer canoes in Temlaham.

Temlaham was waiting.

"But . . . toward the sunrise?" children challenged their elders. Only timbered mountains lay that way, mountains where the Wise Woman of the Woods lived, and the dreaded Ogre.

"We'll skirt the coast southward until a river opens the way inland, toward the sunrise," their elders told them. And, satisfied, the children ran off for more wood or more clams or more water.

At last all was ready. And excitement was tinged with sadness. They were leaving their old home, their old familiar clam beds and berry patches.

But they were leaving for Temlaham!

seven

D AY AFTER DAY AFTER DAY they skirted the coast southward, watching for a river. They followed the protected inside passage, camping and fishing and snaring game along the lee of the big offshore islands. And always their thoughts leaped ahead to the wonders of Temlaham.

At last a river opened the way inland, toward the sunrise.

Alert to the dangers of an unknown, swift-running northern river, they inched their way up its channels. They carried their canoes around its white waters. They camped on its leafy banks. And, always, their keen eyes watched for signs of the coming winter.

Before the first snow fell, they had built good shelters against the coming storms; they had smoked stores of salmon. But it was just a winter camp. For this was not the Promised Land.

"This is not Temlaham," the shaman reminded them as they relaxed around their fires. And now he was like a spent torch, sputtering into brightness before it snuffed out. His skinny old arm pointed toward the sunrise, which was southward as well as eastward in this northern land. "Temlaham is still waiting," he urged them. Then stopped speaking, forever.

The winter was longer and harder than those at the coast. But at long last the ice began to melt and trees began to shake off their snow. Immense tribes of candlefish moved in from the sea. The Northern Lights flared and crackled. Wolves filled the starry night with their songs of mating. And, as if in answer to the call for new life, all along the river the cottonwood buds swelled with the springtime.

Finally the sticky buds burst, flooding the valley with fragrance. Muskrats nosed through the open water, spreading a V of sparkling ripples. And the land was good.

"But it is not Temlaham," they reminded one another. The shaman had said so.

Still, it was a good land; and they waited there until they were well equipped and provisioned, until the days lengthened in the northern valleys. And while they waited, scouts explored animal trails, south and east toward the sunrise.

One moonlit night they were roused from sleep by a trumpeting from the sky. Trembling with fear of the unknown, they crept out. And with eyes wide and mouths even wider, they watched the high passing of ghost-white birds.

"Heaven birds!" they gasped. Passing to the northwest.

"A sign," someone breathed.

"A sign from Temlaham," others agreed. For the Heaven birds had come out of the land that lay southward and eastward. As if in confirmation came another ghostly trumpeting from the sky. And the spirit birds vanished.

Excitement burst out among the people. These must be the Heaven birds of the old tribal tales. They must be a sign from the Promised Land.

Now the scouts moved with renewed eagerness along the trails that led into the mountains and the mountain passes. Now the people sang as they worked on equipment and provisions. Now the plank drums throbbed. Temlaham was waiting, as the shaman had told them.

At last the migrating tribe moved out. And again they moved first toward the south. But this time they moved on foot, along inland trails that seemed wonderfully dry and open and easy after the trails they had known through the dense jungle of the coastal forest.

Always a few women along the trail sang to alert grizzly bears and moose; so that no great beast would be startled into an attack on the travelers. And the warblers sang with them as willow trees and alders began to flash with the reds and yellows, the greens and jet blacks of tiny songbirds. Dark evergreens

49

began to fill with rippling music.

"The Trail to Temlaham," someone would call out, accepting the birds as heralds of the Promised Land.

The trail led on and on and on, through a mountain pass and into an alpine meadow.

"Perhaps this is Temlaham," people said. For the meadow was a sea color, islanded with evergreens and poplar groves. Pink roses and yellow daisies cascaded down the slopes into a foam of white flowers. Great waves of purple and blue lupins met and merged with swells of flaming paintbrush. Hummingbirds, butterflies and honeybees moved above the flowers like miniature seabirds above ocean waves. Perhaps this was the Promised Land.

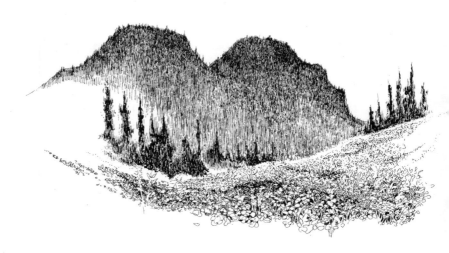

But no. The shaman had seen big rivers in his spirit vision, rivers teeming with salmon. And here there was only a crystal stream tinkling over a rocky bed and flinging rainbow sprays over blue forget-me-nots.

So they moved on, slowly, hunting and camping and scouting the animal trails as they went. And at last they reached a big river, a salmon river!

Eyes brightened at sight of its wide, racing waters. A canoe river, perhaps with access to the sea? And by the river a lovely little prairie where houses could stand facing the river, as their old houses had faced the sea. While all around were mountains where surely the goats were leaping and the eagles circling.

"This is Temlaham," they told one another, their eyes and their voices full of hope.

So the tribe settled down there. Men felled trees for houses and longed for time to make canoes, too. They fished and hunted. Women smoked fish and searched out the berry patches and the good roots. And the summer stars were lovely in the brief Northern Lights.

Then the great salmon run came.

"The shaman's vision!" they breathed, in awe of the teeming plenty of the fish. "This *is* Temlaham."

Men scouted the hills and found the promised plenty there, too; though they lacked time and equipment for a real goat hunt.

When the snows came, and the ice and the bitter winds, they remembered the plenty of hills and rivers. They remembered the flowers and the joyous songbirds. They remembered the Heaven birds. And they dared to call their new home TEMLAHAM.

Then, just as the winter was ending, they saw the STAR. While the Northern Lights flared and crackled, while the wolves filled the night with their songs of mating, they saw the star moving across the sky. Across and down.

"A sign," people gasped, sinking to the earth in sudden terror. Engulfed in memories of the destruction that had come from the Sky, they watched it until it vanished.

"No harm can come to us here, in Temlaham," a chief said in a clear voice.

"If . . . if this *is* Temlaham," a woman whispered to her trembling husband.

The people crept back into their houses. They heaped wood on their fires.

"Perhaps it was a good sign," they told one another.

Then they fell quiet, listening to the high, eerie songs of the wolves.

There was such terrible power out there, in the other world, the world of ghosts, spirits, and supernatural Beings.

eight

AGAIN THE "STAR" WAS A TLU SPACESHIP.

This time it was on a different sort of rescue mission. This time the threat was not to Earth colonists, but to the entire population of Tlu. The home planet was doomed.

Pictures of Earth's grasslands and forests were being studied in stark cities. Earth data banks were whirring and flashing. For, suddenly, Tluan technologists had seen Doomsday looming on their own horizon. They had seen warning signs for decades. But now, suddenly, they were faced with alarming statistics. The green growing things of Tlu were headed for extermination. And the ETA (estimated time of arrival) of Doomsday was 102 years away.

Immediate corrective measures were indicated. This time a ruthless slash of Tlu population would not be enough. The planet itself needed a green transfusion. Earth was a suitable donor. The green transfusions would be administered to the sick planet through a number of small Earth Parks.

The plan for the regreening of Tlu had been instantly activated. A ship was dispatched to Earth. A Tluan space freighter was sent to bring back soil, seed, and seedlings from the still-life-rich planet. Other freighters were assigned to the project.

The "star" was the first of the freighters.

Laetl was not in command of any of the ships. His career had ended.

Word of his interest in spirits had leaked out. "Laetlogic," the news media had dubbed it, when it was suggested that he believed plants had spirits that needed tending.

Danger signals had flashed in Tlu's Upper Council. State Heroes could not seriously suggest that Tlu try promoting plant growth by the importation of "witch doctors" with "spirit power." Superstitious nonsense like that could confuse disciplined minds. It could imperil the vital project.

Laetl was eliminated.

The reaction to his elimination brought more danger signals to the UC. Psycho-puters recorded a rash of sightings of "misty, miniature hominoid forms."

"Mass hysteria," the psycho-puters diagnosed. "Perceptual aberrations due to stress factors connected with the recent alarming deceleration of plant growth." It was an epidemic of brain malfunctions.

The logical minds of the UC decided to divert the populace with new input. They announced that semipermanent stations were to be set up on Earth. The stations were to be staffed by plant, soil and computer experts. The experts would analyze Earth plants for their suitability to Tluan conditions.

Staff movement around Earth would be optimized by new electromagnetic disk craft. These silvery disks had a system of rotation that enabled them to tap Earth's magnetic fields. This eliminated all problems of propellant fuel. Too, their operation was almost silent. So they would cause little alarm among the natives. They would arouse the least hostility. In fact, luminosity and corona discharges caused by speedup could well be mistaken by ignorant savages for natural Earth phenomena, like the Northern Lights.

Tlumen did not seem very interested in the new electromagnetic marvels. It was Laetl's spirits that had caught public fancy. People still claimed to see small, misty beings.

"Laetloonies," the news media dubbed the sighters.

"Escape into fantasy due to anxiety," the psychoputers said. "Regression to primitive thinking."

A number of eliminations put an end to the sightings.

A UC media release put an end to all mention of "Laetloonies." The release pointed out that Laetl had had an unblemished record of service to Tlu. He had suffered severe stress on his final command. And his tragic hallucinations were not to become a subject for public witticisms.

The media instantly dropped all reference to spirits. And to save their skins, the Laetloonies went underground. In small, cautious groups they haunted Tlu's doomed farms. They secretly tried to invoke the witch doctors' spirits.

"It is logical," was their secret password. Laetl had said that Earth farmers invoked spirits. Their corn flourished. So there was a possibility that plants did have a spirit. There was a possibility that these spirits demanded deference from the people they fed.

"Savage ritual," the UC called it when the first case of communing-with-spirits was uncovered and punished. "Primitive practice unworthy of an intellectual, properly unemotional society." "Spirits" were a concept rejected by the computer.

"How would a computer know?" the rebels pointed out to one another. "A computer's output is limited by its input."

A man's output, too, was limited by his input, they reminded one another. And to insure a "spirit" input in Tlumen's logical minds, they took to scribbling on walls. They drew pictures of computers being chased by tree spirits.

"It is logical," they assured one another.

The UC issued a series of articles written by its experts. The articles stressed the fact that a tree or a blade of grass was basically an industrial plant operating under the universal laws of science. It housed many machines, called cells. Powered by energy from

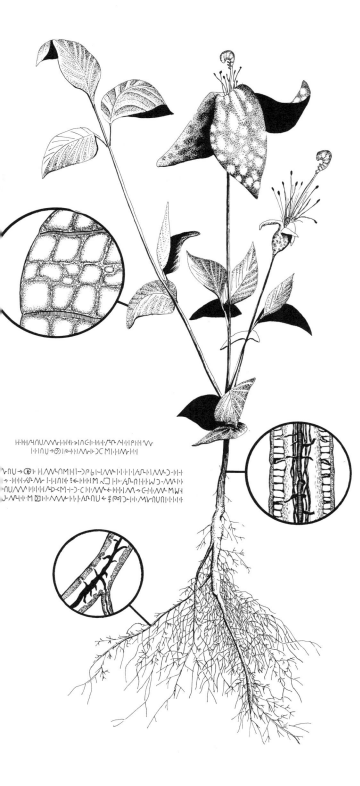

the sun, these machines took in the raw products: carbon dioxide and water. They turned out the finished products: carbohydrates to nourish animal life on the planet, and oxygen to renew the atmosphere's supply every 2,000 years.

At the moment, Tlu's natural plants were malfunctioning. But scientists would track down the malfunction and correct it. They would get the machines producing again at full capacity. And the entire population must get behind this effort to save the planet. Anyone who did not get behind it would be eliminated.

Members of the underground simply kept their mouths shut, and became more secretive about their acceptance of Laetlogic. And they dreamed of making a trip to Earth, where everyone believed in spirits.

There could be little contact with those Earthmen, of course. Station personnel were to avoid contact wherever possible. Where it was not possible, Earthmen were to be confirmed in their belief that Tlumen were Gods-from-the-Sky. That way, there would be little interference.

Nevertheless, the Laetloonies dreamed of contact with people who believed in spirits.

nine

THE MOVING "STAR" WAS A GOOD SIGN, the shamans had decided. And, unaware that any but supernatural beings lived out there beyond their own world, the coastal people settled into their new home.

They taught their children, as they had always taught them, that every living thing had a spirit Self as well as a physical being; and it was the spirit Self that controlled the being. It was the spirit Self of a tree or a salmon or a sea lion that had to be appeased if need forced you to do harm to the body it was animating at the time of your need.

Joined from time to time by other straggling bands from the coast, they built fine cedar houses on the

little prairie by the river. And on each housefront they painted a traditional kinship crest: Eagle, Wolf, Bear or Raven. On the portal poles that reached above the houses, they carved and painted other cherished family emblems: Frog, Beaver, Killer Whale, Fireweed. . . . Even their canoes grew bright with the heraldry of a prospering northern people.

Moving among their houses, they looked proud and confident. Like people who knew they were Chosen People. Like people who knew that, for them, there would always be peace and plenty.

As the years went by, as the peace and plenty continued, a few people grew overconfident. A few forgot their proper reverence toward the world of nature spirits, a world far more powerful than even the most prospering people.

One year, as always, the golden leaves of autumn and the hazy blue of the mountains foretold the coming of winter. But what of that? people's glances seemed to say. Their food boxes would be filled to overflowing. For this was Temlaham, the Promised Land.

Salmon were running up the river to the spawning creeks. And at the tribal fishing stations, men were busy with spears and dip nets; women were busy with smoke and fish knives; children were fetching and carrying and watching the salmon.

Only four youths lolled in the shade of a poplar, as Say-ok had lolled by the drift stump. Their hair and ear ornaments marked them, too, as of high rank, while tattoos showed them to be nobles of the Raven Crest.

Careless of reproving looks from their elders, they laughed uproariously at their leader's jokes. Until, finally, an old man made his way toward the lazy youths. An old man of their own Crest.

"The Bear Prince is fishing," he pointed out sharply, indicating a young man on a fishing platform near the mouth of the canyon.

"Good for him!" The Raven Prince tossed his flip answer at the old man, then went on with the joke he was telling.

But the old man persisted in trying to shame them out of their laziness. "You plan to feed your people on jokes when the storms come?" he suggested, his voice tart as a crabapple.

"Of course. It's noble to eat sparingly," the Raven Prince retorted, winking at his own wit.

"I thought you didn't know that," the old man shot back. "I have often observed that your appetite is like Raven's."

The youth flushed at this reference to the mythical Glutton. But he maintained his defiance. "You live by old tales, old man. By superstitious nonsense."

"And since you do," a friend added slyly, "beware, old man! Remember what happened to the people who once ridiculed a prince. Prince Filthy, you remember?"

Winking approvingly at his friend, the prince got lazily to his feet. "Let's leave the Bear Prince to catch every fish in the river," he suggested to the youths, who were not only his friends but also his official attendants.

The others rose instantly. "Of course a few will get away," one of the three said.

"That gives me an idea," the prince answered. "Let's have some sport with the ones that are smart enough to get away from the noble Bear."

Have sport with salmon? The friends felt some concern. But he was the prince. Besides, his audacious ways made life very interesting.

Still . . .

There was reluctance in their steps as they followed him along the trail that led, finally, to a spawning creek. And there they stood watching the salmon make their way upstream, against the race of the shallow water.

The eyes of the youngest boy betrayed his feeling for the salmon. Though the fishes' bodies were almost spent from the long struggle against currents and canyons and waterfalls, the great spirit Selves of the salmon hurtled them valiantly on, over the spawning gravel. For they could not drop their eggs or their fertilizing milt until they had reached the spot where the life of these bodies had started. They had to complete the mysterious cycle of the salmon, decreed by the Great Salmon Spirit.

Across the creek, farther upstream, a family of bears cuffed at the struggling bodies. Like people and otters and eagles all along the river, bears depended on the salmon.

"Huh!" the prince joked. "They've escaped from one Bear only to be done in by another."

The youngest attendant guffawed loudly, hoping that his prince would content himself with wit. It

would be terrible to hurt the salmon and offend the spirit world.

Instead, the guffaw seemed to spur on the leader. "Hey! Fish!" he called out to a big, hurtling salmon. "Maybe I should save you from all the Bears." And with the sort of savage outburst that marked most of his great ideas, the Raven Prince grabbed up a rock and hurled it at the silver body. And when he missed, he grabbed up three more rocks and hurled them in furious succession.

The salmon flopped. And lay still.

A shocked silence followed. And three small boys, peering out from behind bushes at the rebel prince and his friends, clapped their hands over their mouths so that their gasps would not be heard. No one ever dared to make sport of a salmon. The salmon spirits might be offended and leave the river forever.

The Raven Prince picked up another rock and said, "Well?" to his craven attendants, who then picked up rocks, too, to prove they weren't craven.

The youngest boy threw his rock to miss, feeling doubly craven. For he was truly afraid of angering the Great Salmon Spirit.

"I have a better idea," the brash leader announced when his first idea seemed to be falling flat. And calling, "Stay there!" he sprinted off into the woods.

By and by he came back with bits of pitch pine. "A little plan to scare off the Bear Clan," he said, nodding toward the family of bears. "Light this!" he ordered his youngest attendant, thrusting a bit of pitch pine at him, along with the live coal he carried in a big clamshell fire holder.

64

Then, with his two other friends' help, he swooped up a big, struggling salmon and made a cut in its back.

Next, he inserted a flaming torch of pitch pine in the cut. "There! Go scare the Bears!" he said, putting it back into the water.

The peeping boys again clapped their hands over their gasps as torch after torch was sent flaring up the riffles.

Then . . .

The Earth shook.

Rocks tumbled down a mountain to the north.

The small boys fled in terror, straight to their families. And the big boys passed them on the way.

People were standing in huddles, facing north, and there was horror on their faces.

"What did we do?" they were asking one another.

The three small boys made explosive noises. They glanced fearfully at the prince who had been so arrogant and who was now trembling.

The old man made his way toward the quaking prince. "What did you do?" he demanded.

And with the eyes of the whole village on him, the Raven Prince tumbled out his story. Fearful of yet worse retaliation from the offended spirits, he confessed his sin and threw himself into an agony of ceremonial appeasement, in which his attendants joined him.

Engulfed by tribal memory of the cataclysm that had come before, people cast anxious glances at the Sky. More shaken than the earth, they waited . . . and waited . . . and waited for worse to happen.

But nothing else happened. Except to the offending

prince and his attendants. They were stripped of their rank in public ceremony, and made slaves with shorn hair, in the hope that their public disgrace would appease the Great Salmon Spirit.

"Perhaps nothing more will happen," the people began to hope. "Perhaps this was just a sign, a warning."

And so it seemed. For nothing further happened.

But it was a warning to make men tremble. A terrifying power was out there, even in Temlaham.

ten

THE YEARS HAD BEEN LESS PROSPEROUS IN TLU.

Trees, shrubs, corn, grass, and flowers grew in the Earth Parks. But they did not grow as vigorously as they had grown on Earth. There was some malfunction in the green transfusion system.

ETA of Doomsday was now seventy-eight years away.

The population was slashed again. Farm staffs were doubled. Cities were full of gloom.

"Any idea should be tried," people whispered to one another. They recalled Laetlogic. And they found it reasonable.

There *was* the possibility of gaps in Tluan information. There *was* the possibility that Tluan specialists had received an incomplete input of information. And this lack of complete information had limited their diagnoses of plant problems. After all, a man, like a computer, was a prisoner of his program. Tlumen were programmed to a mechanistic view of plant life. They were not equipped to consider the spirit beings Earth farmers called upon. Yet spirits could be a fact.

There was an underground swell of Laetloonies. A group of young people gained access to old Earth films. They secretively watched witch doctors invoking corn spirits. And their hungry eyes gazed at the subsequent harvest.

They watched film on corn-spirit dances. And they recalled Laetl's theory. It was the strange emotion; the strange dancing and drumming keyed primitive senses up to a frequency that enabled them to tune into the spirit world.

As a logical sequence to such discussions, they experimented with primitive dancing. Bodies leaped and whirled in the dead of night. Voices chanted.

One young woman saw a strange, misty radiance in Earth Park plants.

The UC patrol saw her. She was taken into custody.

"A hallucination," the psycho-puters called it. "A regression to primitive thinking due to anxiety factors."

A regression to primitive thinking was dangerous to a high, technological society, the UC decreed. The young woman was eliminated. The dancing stopped.

Three young people experimented with high frequency photography. That was acceptable to a high, technological society. They captured the radiance on film. There was a flaring, ethereal body of colored light that interpenetrated the body of the plant and surrounded it with a living, flaring luminosity.

So it had not been hallucination. There *was* something more to plants than the microscopes had discovered and the lab scales had weighed. Trees and grasses were more than industrial plants, which housed machines that took in the raw products—carbon dioxide and water—and turned out the finished products—carbohydrates to nourish animal life, and oxygen to renew the atmosphere's supply.

So, logical minds theorized, there was a possibility that Earthmen were right. There was a possibility that the spirit world was a cosmic fact. Spirit Beings might be promoting their plants' growth.

Faced with the high frequency photographs of a misty radiance flaring out of plants, UC experts backed down a little.

"There may be a form of hitherto undiscovered bioplasmic energy in plants," they admitted. But to endow bioplasmic energy with the consciousness of spirit beings was to regress to the primitive concept of animism. It showed a dangerous weakness in logical thinking.

Experiments were to be discontinued by the lay public. The properly trained scientific community would conduct all the experiments deemed necessary.

But here was a new frontier for a science, rebels noted to one another. Here was a challenging new frontier, if only the properly trained scientific community would unscrew all the nuts and bolts that were keeping its minds closed. Here might well be the last hope for the regreening of Tlu and the survival of its people.

The rebels did the logical thing. They quietly infiltrated the ranks of specialists bound for the Earth stations.

There they could don rocket belts and zoom into wilderness areas to continue their experiments. There they could eavesdrop electronically on people who believed in a spirit world. They could not make full contact, of course. UC decrees were strict on that matter. Contact with Earthmen was to be avoided. Where it could not be avoided, Earthmen were to be encouraged in their belief that Tlumen were Gods who must not be interfered with.

Still, with luck, they could find out how to cancel Doomsday.

eleven

UNAWARE THAT AN ALIEN PEOPLE HAD COME to their world, the Temlahams were alarmed when strange Beings began to appear on their skyline.

Dwarfing the eagles, the Beings thundered in and out of a not-too-distant mountain. Moving mainly at dawn and dusk, they further terrified people with flashes of lightning.

"Sky Beings," the Temlahams fearfully agreed. "*Naq noqs* of the Air. Supernatural Thunderbirds." And they trembled when they glimpsed one, for tribal storytellers had never let them forget the awesome powers possessed by Sky Beings.

A boy who had been alone in the hills, seeking

his spirit power, claimed to have glimpsed a face peering out at him from behind a bush—a face like a man's, though with skin as pale as a peeled log and with hair as golden as the sun. A Thunderbird in human disguise? they wondered; for supernatural Beings could take on human form.

As time went on, though, and the Thunderbirds came no closer, people drifted back to other troubles.

After the affair of the salmon-torches-and-the-earthquake, the Bear clans seemed to have wrapped their virtue around them like a rich cloak; and of all the Bear clans, the Fireweeds were the most virtuous. At the same time, the Raven groups showed a growing defiance of the Old Way; and of all the Raven clans, the group directly across the river from the Fireweeds was the most defiant. The highest ranking of the young Raven nobles openly boasted of his success with the wife of the highest ranking of the young Fireweed nobles.

One night, when a sudden, bitter cold spell had iced-over the river between the two villages, the Raven houses rang with the rattle of gambling sticks and the chanting of the game.

The Fireweed houses were ominously quiet.

Inside the biggest of the Fireweed houses, a group of high ranking people huddled near the fire. And the lesser people held themselves in silence back in the shadows of the huge, windowless house.

"O my son! My dear son!" a woman by the fire moaned, rocking herself in grief.

"He will be avenged," her remaining three sons told her.

72

The Chief entered the house and glided toward them. "Tell me!" he commanded.

One of the sons answered. "The beaver dam caved in while we were hunting, and our brother was drowned."

"Who put the evil spell on him?" the Chief demanded in a fierce whisper. For always a hunter's death was really caused by an evil-wisher. "Who broke the hunting taboos?"

"His wife!" the mother burst out. "Instead of fasting and praying and chewing devil's club roots as a hunter's wife must to please the spirits, she has spent the nights carousing with her Raven lover."

"Tonight the carousing stops," the eldest brother announced, slipping out into the night as silently as an owl. And when he did not return, the second brother slipped out, and then the third brother, leaving an awful, waiting silence. For the lover was the highest ranking of all the young Raven men; and his death would be fiercely avenged. War would shatter the uneasy peace of Temlaham.

The silence held until the youngest brother returned, alone. Then it was broken by gasps. For on his spear was the bleeding head of the young Raven noble.

Horrified eyes watched as he placed the gruesome head on the beams over the doorway.

"Now! Take Skawah to safety!" he urged them.

Skawah, his sister, was the highest ranking of the Fireweed girls. She carried the royal bloodline. She must survive to carry on the great line of Fireweed Chiefs. Too, she must survive to raise heirs to avenge

73

the Fireweeds if the treacherous Ravens managed to massacre them. Survival of the lineage was a sacred duty, as blood revenge was a sacred duty. The peace of family ghosts depended on both.

Quickly, Skawah and her mother were led to the secret escape passage at the rear of the house. They were given careful instructions about food caches and shelters in the hills. And they were warmly wrapped against the growing bitterness of the night.

Then the Fireweeds settled into a tense wait for the first move from the Raven people. All night the tense quiet held, and well into the next morning.

Then a slave woman arrived from the Raven village with an unlit torch. The Raven fires had all gone out, she told the Fireweeds. And they, knowing full well that she had come only to spy, allowed her to light her torch from their fire; for a neighbor must always be allowed to borrow fire. They held their breaths as she lingered near the doorway, blowing on her torch, as if she feared it might go out.

They saw the drop of blood fall from the beams above her. They saw her rush out as if she must get the fire to the Ravens at once. And they exchanged dark looks. Mothers clutched their children to them.

Shrieking like the evil spirits of a storm, the inflamed Ravens rushed across the ice. And by nightfall every Fireweed man, woman, and child had been killed; every Fireweed house flamed in the rising wind.

By dawn, only the wind and the ghosts howled above the smoldering ruins of the once-proud village.

74

Forlorn in their shelter in the hills, Skawah and her mother saw the whipping smoke, as they had seen the flames. But only Skawah saw the terrifying sign, the disk of light, pale as the moon, racing into the mountains where the Thunderbirds lived. A sign from the Sky! But what more could happen to the Fireweeds?

"O my sons! My dear sons!" her mother was moaning as she rocked herself in the shelter. "And my poor murdered kinsmen! Their ghosts float now above the ashes of our houses. And they will float there forever, for there is no one to avenge their death."

"Mother!" Skawah protested gently. "There will be men to avenge their deaths and free their ghosts to travel on, when I have children." Perhaps that was what the sign had meant. Perhaps it had been a good sign.

"Who will marry you?" her mother wailed. "A girl with no relatives to arrange a marriage. A princess with no home, no wealth. Who will marry a girl whose uncles are ghosts drifting unavenged above the ashes of their houses? Who will marry you?"

Patient with her grieving mother, Skawah searched for firewood, food, and new shelters all through the bitter winter. She blackened her skin with mourning ashes and kept herself warm with mourning tatters. She kept them alive until the trees gently shook off their snow, and birds and mating wolves began to sing, and buds began to swell on the poplars.

Then she saw the sign again.

twelve

AGAIN, ONLY SHE SAW THE DISK, shining pale as the moon in the cold dawn.

It was a sign to her, to remind her of her sacred duty to her murdered kinsmen. For only she could bring peace to their ghosts.

"O my sons! My dear sons!" her mother still moaned, rocking herself in the shelter. "Oh, all my murdered kinsmen whose ghosts float now above the ashes of our houses! Whose ghosts will float there forever, because there is no one to avenge their deaths and free them to travel on."

"Mother!" Skawah protested, as she had protested a thousand times. "There will be men to avenge their deaths and free their ghosts, when I have children."

"Who will marry you?" her mother wailed, as she had wailed a thousand times.

"Yes," Skawah agreed with sudden spirit. "Who will marry me while I roam the hills, black with mourning ashes and aflutter with mourning tatters? Mother! It's springtime! The birds are singing. Life is stirring again." She ran to a stream and washed herself. Then she opened a treasured bundle and shook out a white robe of weasel skins. She held up abalone shell earrings, turning them to catch their rainbow iridescence.

When she had put them on, she turned herself slowly about in the sunshine. Then, holding out her arms to the world, she called out, "Who will marry me?"

Startled by a flash, and a roll of thunder, she spun around, toward the mountain.

"A Thunderbird?" she gasped. But the swift dark form had been swallowed by the timbered hills.

Was that what the sign had meant?

"Mother?" she breathed, her eyes wide with awe. "Mother! A Thunderbird will marry me!" There had been many strange matings in the old tribal stories. Many supernatural Beings had taken on human form to marry a princess, back in the days of very long ago. Perhaps it could still happen.

"No one will marry you," her mother moaned. "You? A girl with no home, no family, no wealth. No one will marry you. So our ghosts will drift forever, unavenged above the ashes."

Sadly, the girl put her white robe and earrings

back into the bundle. And the two wandered on, finding food, firewood, and new shelters as they went.

But again, when the trees had burst into leaf and birds were singing in an ecstasy of springtime and mating, Skawah washed herself and donned her finery. And once more she turned herself in the sunshine, holding out her arms. "Who will marry me?" she called out.

A man stepped from the shadow of a tree.

"I will marry you, Skawah," he said, in halting tones, as if his tongue were not accustomed to human speech.

"A *naq noq!*" her mother gasped; and her eyes widened in terror. For he was not a true man. His skin was as pale as a peeled log. His hair was golden as the sun. And his blindingly white garments flashed in the sunlight, like licking tongues of fire.

The women trembled back from him.

"I have come from the Sky," he told them. And his eyes were as blue as the Sky he had come from.

Speaking directly to the mother, he said, "I wish to marry Skawah." Then, turning to the princess, he repeated the words softly, "I wish to marry Skawah."

His gaze moved over her shining black hair, her soft brown eyes, her slender rounded form as if she were some strange and exotic flower. And she felt herself responding as a flower responds to sunbeams.

"Sunbeams!" the girl breathed, knowing now what he was. He *was* from the Sky. He was a Sun Being who had taken on human form to marry her. For it was as though a flood of light and warmth flowed into her from him. She felt as though sunbeams were dancing over her body. "You are Sunbeams," she said, suddenly smiling at him. And he nodded in surprise. He had not known that she would recognize him for what he really was, in his true form.

Her mother was still shocked by the approach of a supernatural suitor. But she was not too shocked to remember that the bride's family did not shame itself with instant agreement to an offer of marriage. Dignity demanded slow, courteous negotiations.

"Man-from-the-Sky," she said, "my daughter has a sacred duty, her duty to her lineage. What could you do to help her with this duty? What power have you, Man-from-the-Sky?"

The man took a strange, bright rod from his garments. He pointed it at a tree across the mountain valley, a lone tree on a rock. "Turn away and cover your eyes!" he commanded.

They sensed the flash. And when they had opened their eyes again, the tree had vanished. It had utterly vanished from the rock.

Both women sank to the ground, quaking like aspens in a breeze. But the mother soon recovered herself enough to continue the proper negotiations for her daughter's marriage.

"You have other powers, Man-from-the-Sky?"

He smiled at Skawah. And again it was as if warmth and light flooded into her, as if sunbeams were dancing over her body. Then he drew a small box out of his strange, bright garments. And when he had walked a distance away from them, he held it up. And the Earth shook. Across the valley, rocks tumbled down the mountainside.

80

Again the women sank to the ground, quaking like aspens.

The Man-from-the-Sky returned and smiled at them. "I wish to marry Skawah," he said.

"Marry Skawah!" her mother agreed. And her mind was filled with thoughts of what would happen to the Ravens when this man's sons, and Skawah's, were ready for their sacred duty.

"Then come!" the man said. "I must prepare you for the flight." There was a brightness of light, he explained; so their eyes must be shielded, their faces covered. And they understood that he meant the fierce, close light of the sun, the light of Skyland.

"I am too old," the mother objected. "I am too old and weary to make such a journey."

"Then we can't go," Skawah said to the young man; and her voice was sad with regret.

"You will go!" her mother thundered at her.

"But you—"

"Your duty is not to me," her mother reminded her fiercely. "Your sacred duty is to the ghosts of our murdered kinsmen. You must insure their vengeance. You must insure the survival of their lineage. Your duty is to the Fireweeds, all the Fireweeds!"

So Skawah went.

thirteen

THREE RAVEN MEN SAW THE *thing* lift out of the mountains where the Thunderbirds lived. And they trembled in the chill dawn. It was round, like the sun; it glowed with a yellow light; and yellow light flared from it. Then it paled as it vanished into the Sky.

"A sign!" they gasped, and raced into their Chief's house.

"A sign from the Sky!" people muttered, aghast.

Tribal memory of the terrible things that had come from the Sky overwhelmed them with dread.

"We should not have killed all the Fireweeds," they whispered to one another. For the Fireweeds had been their own tribesmen. There had been many ties of kinship.

Gripped by terror, they waited for something to happen.

But nothing happened. Spring turned into summer and nothing happened. Flowers bloomed. Berries ripened. Fish came up the river. And still nothing happened. The leaves turned to gold. Goats leaped on the mountains. The snow fell. And nothing happened. Storms howled around their houses, as they had always howled. The Northern Lights flared and crackled. Wolves filled the night with their songs of mating. The buds swelled on the trees. And still nothing happened.

"The sign was not for us," the people began to tell one another.

And so it seemed. For years passed. And still nothing bad happened to the Ravens.

"But the ghosts are still there," they whispered sometimes at night, when the wind carried eerie sounds across the river.

"What can ghosts do?" a few brash people began to ask. And they began to boast of what they had done. For had they not wiped out the proudest clan in Temlaham?

Now, who could stop them? For, as they began to lay claim to the Fireweed fishing stations and the Fireweed hunting huts, their prosperity grew. Their houses became bigger, their canoes more numerous.

One summer evening, many years later, their houses were loud with the rattle-and-chant of gambling; while across the river there was nothing but silent desolation. Where houses had stood, now there were only the thrusting spires of fireweed, stirring in the breeze as though whispering the hopes of the still-drifting, still-unavenged ghosts of the people who had lived there.

Then, suddenly, two boys rushed into the Chief's house, where the gambling was loudest. "We saw the sign again," they said full of excitement. All their lives they had heard about the sign.

But when the people rushed out, there was a strange mist shrouding the Sky. Strangely for that time of year, a thick, white mist was gathering on the river; it was spreading slowly around the Raven houses.

"A strange mist!" an old man said, groping his way through it.

"A good mist!" a young man answered, with a show of bravado. "It will keep everyone indoors for a great night of gambling."

And so it seemed. For soon the biggest of the Raven houses was loud with guffaws.

Yet there was a tenseness in the watching women. They clutched their children to them.

The old man stayed apart, listening . . . listening . . . listening. His ear leaned toward the river, listening . . . listening.

"Listen!" he cried out. "There are sounds across the river."

"Perhaps the ghosts are finally taking off," a young noble joked.

"Beware!" the old man warned. "Beware how you speak of the dead! The Chiefs of the spirit world are mighty."

"Mighty slow," the young man agreed, going back to his gambling. "You've been warning us for ages, and nothing has happened. Nothing is going to happen. The Fireweeds are finished."

But something was happening across the river.

"Listen!" the old man called out again.

This time the hushed people heard sounds of bumping and hammering. A few bold ones ventured out; but the world was still shrouded in the strange, thick fog.

Uneasy now, men stirred up the fire in the center of the great, shadowy house. Women busied themselves with food. And the young men gambled more quietly.

The old man kept his ear toward the river. And many joined him in his tense listening . . . listening.

"Listen!" people began to whisper to one another. "Perhaps the dead have come back to life to rebuild their houses." For the sounds were uncannily like the sounds of house-building.

"Or perhaps . . ." an old woman suggested. "Perhaps the Fireweeds are not all dead."

"Not all dead?" There had been nothing but smoking ashes after the battle.

"Perhaps the girl Skawah escaped," the old woman went on. For no one had dared to poke about among the ashes.

"Perhaps she did escape," other people began to agree. For they, too, would have planned for the survival of their highest bloodline. "And perhaps she has returned with warriors." For they, too, would have planned to return to avenge their dead kinsmen.

A terrible silence settled down on the Raven houses. People waited for morning. Waited . . . and waited . . . and waited, with growing dread of what they would see across the river. But they scarcely knew when it was morning. For the strange fog lingered, too thick for the sun to dissipate. And the noises continued across the river.

Then, at long last, the uncanny fog began to thin out a little. And the people peered across the river, with ever increasing dread.

There was a brightness across the river, making the fog luminous above the spot where the ashes had been. There were beams of light flaring out of the luminous cloud. And there was a strange, humming sound.

"The Northern Lights!" people gasped. But the Northern Lights belonged on the far horizon, not on the bank of their river. And the sounds were different.

The glow and the terrifying lights lifted and moved away behind the shrouding of fog. Until suddenly it was like a star, a star moving off behind a ghost shroud.

People sank to the ground, trembling.

Then they saw the houses emerging from the mist. And they cowered back toward their own houses.

Suddenly the sun broke through, and the people gazed, stunned, at what they saw.

Now, facing them across the river—where yesterday there had been only fireweeds waving in the desolation—were four houses, four strangely bright houses. And on every housefront was a crest: Sun, Star, Rainbow, and Thunderbird. Totem crests never before seen!

Beings moved about among the houses. They were like people. Yet . . . Yet their garments had a strange brightness.

"*Naq noqs*," people whispered, trembling.

"Sky spirits," others agreed; for were not their crests from the Sky?

"Sky spirits?" More than once, in the days of very long ago, destruction had come from the Sky.

The night increased their dread of the Beings across the river. For when the world darkened, the Sky crests across the river shone out with ghostly luminescence: Sun, Star, Rainbow, and Thunderbird.

The Ravens huddled together in terror.

For days and nights and days and nights they huddled together, peering furtively at the *naq noqs* across the river.

It was three Raven children who finally sneaked across the river, one evening when their parents were busy.

"They're real people," they reported to their stunned relatives.

But the relatives only clutched the children to them and waited for something dreadful to happen to them.

When time went by and nothing happened to the children, a slave woman was dispatched across the river to borrow fire. And the Ravens waited for her return with fear and trembling.

But the slave woman returned with fire and a gift

of food.

"Ghost food!" people gasped, shrinking back from it. Ghost food was death to the living.

A child sneaked a taste, and then told his horrified elders, who waited to see him drop dead.

But nothing happened to this child either.

"They're not ghosts," the people began to say.

"Maybe they're not even *naq noqs*."

Dread began to dissipate, as the mists had dissipated. Canoes began to move out again. Men gambled again, and boasted.

But the boasting was hollow, for the danger was clear.

"Skawah did escape," They told one another. "And she has returned to avenge her dead kinsmen."

But who had married Skawah? A supernatural Being? A Sky Being? And what power did she now possess? What power to wreak vengeance?

So the Ravens alerted themselves for the first sign of revenge. They kept careful watch on their old enemies across the river. They waited . . . and waited . . .

And as they waited, they prepared themselves for battle.

fourteen

CROSS THE RIVER, in the new-old Fireweed village, Skawah was as anxious as any Raven.

"There are so many of them!" she kept moaning.

"Then why must we attack them?" her younger
daughter asked her.

"Because it is our sacred duty to our murdered
kinsmen. Until they are avenged, their ghosts hover
about us, like driftwood in the water."

"But we'll all be killed," the daughter protested.

"Perhaps not," Skawah answered mysteriously.

"Earth is so lovely!" the girl went on, yearning
over the beauty of trees, river, and mountains.
"Mother, we have another duty." She pointed Skyward.

"To the laws of your father's people?" Skawah dismissed them with her hand. "Here, children belong to their mother's family; they are bound by their laws."

The daughter sighed. "It's so lovely and quiet here."

"Too quiet!" Skawah snapped. "Tonight they will attack us."

"But Mother! Why should they attack us?"

"Because they know we will attack them when we are ready. And because they are in dread of the powers we may have brought with us from Skyland, they will attack us before we are ready." Her eyes narrowed. Her voice gathered fierce strength. "Well may they dread our Sky power!"

"What do you mean, Mother?"

"You will see when the time comes," Skawah answered. And she slipped off to the house.

The girl stayed on by the river, gazing at the lovely, glistening poplars. Here the world was so soft and green and quiet! "The Promised Land," she murmured. So restful and fresh after the harsh light of Skyland.

Skyland. She remembered the old man they had all called "Grandfather." He would have loved the glistening poplars.

"Grandfather," she whispered, glancing Skyward. "Why didn't you come with us?" He had been a strange old man, always thinking of trees and grasses. In a hard, hot land, he had talked always of greenness. "Why didn't you come with us?" Then she caught her breath. For she seemed to hear his voice again. It seemed to call to her now as it had called, that last time.

"Be good to your Earth!" the kind old voice had implored them. And they had wondered what he meant. "Do not abuse animals!" he had said. And they had understood that, for Skawah had told them that, too. "Above all, spare their broods!" Though he was not of their Earth, he had loved to hear Skawah talk of Temlaham and the endless green forests. "Cherish growth!" he had urged them. "Do not spoil the living green beauty of Earth."

"How could we spoil the living green beauty of Earth?" Skawah had wondered. But she had loved the old man, too.

"The living green beauty of Earth," the girl echoed softly. And her gaze swept over the glistening poplars by the river, and on to the timbered slopes of mountains that were touched by the rosiness of sunset. Then she glimpsed her mother, slipping secretively away from the house. And her eyes clouded. Skawah was planning something.

Silent as an owl, Skawah stole away from the house with something concealed under her robe. She made her way to a spot that gave her a perfect view of the Raven houses, while she herself was lost in shadows. And as she sat watching the sun set, her eyes dimmed with tears.

"Sunbeams," she whispered yearningly, remembering the brightness of his hair and his smile that day when she had met him in the mountains. Then, she had felt as though sunbeams were dancing over her body.

She had gone with him gladly on the terrifying flight. But then she had seen so little of him. Always he had been setting off on yet another journey in his round, glowing Sky craft, moving like a lesser Sun. Always he had left her confined to her lonely quarters, with only the old man and her children to keep her company.

She knew that his people had kept him from her —from her, a woman who had brought no wealth, no family honor to the union. They had kept her apart, as if she had indeed been unworthy. They had not understood the meaning of her ear ornaments . . . of her white weasel robe. No doubt they had thought her a slave woman unworthy of acceptance by the family.

So often, alone in the harsh brightness of Skyland, she had longed for the glistening poplars by the river and for the hazy blue of the timbered, snow-topped mountains. Sometimes the old man had taken her to look down into the magic hole. It was a strange hole. In it she had glimpsed the tops of timbered mountains. As if she had been a soaring eagle. She had seen people below her, moving like ants along old, familiar trails. But she had always known that it was only a spirit vision, like a reflection in a still lake, captured by Sky magic. The hills of home had not really been there.

The old man had done what he could to make her sons strong and skillful. And whenever Sunbeams had slipped in secretively to be with her, she had continued to feel as though sunbeams were dancing over her body. But always by morning he had vanished.

At last he had let her go home, home to the sacred duty that had haunted her night and day, home to Temlaham where she and her children belonged. He himself had gone away to some distant part of Sky-land. She would never again see Sunbeams.

Shadows darkened over the land. And across the river, Ravens vanished into their houses.

Skawah was left alone with her ghosts, the ghosts of her murdered kinsmen. As surely as if she saw them, she knew they were there, waiting for her to free them to cross the mist-bridge into the Land of Ghosts.

"I have not forgotten my sacred duty," she whispered to them. And from under her robe she drew out a small box.

"You showed me this," she said, holding it up toward the sky. "Long ago, when you said that you wished to marry me, and my mother asked you what you could do to help me with my sacred duty—my duty to my murdered kinsmen—you showed me this. And you showed me what it could do."

Remembering how glad and glowing he had looked that day, Skawah shook off tears. She had seen him so seldom after that day. Left to her loneliness and her longing for her old home, she had filled her life with purpose. She had reared her children with that single purpose, the sacred duty for which she had been spared when her people were massacred. Now the time had come.

As night settled over the river, Skawah waited, peering across the river.

Suddenly her body stiffened. For men were creeping stealthily out of the Raven houses. Men armed for battle.

"There are so many of them!" she moaned to the Sky. "And our sons are so young and untried!" She glanced at the houses where her children slept.

Then, once more, she held the box up to the Sky. "You gave me this. For use only in desperate need, you said. Well, now the need is desperate. Is it not desperate when men steal out of their houses to cross the river and murder our sons and daughters? Our sons who are too young and too new to the ways of this land. And our daughters who must survive, as I survived, to carry on the Fireweed bloodline. Is this not desperate need, Sunbeams?"

Just as the moon left a cloud, she leaped out of the shadows. She gave the fierce war whoop of the Fireweeds. She held up the box; and it glinted in the moonlight.

"Beware!" she screamed at the men across the river. "Beware how you attack the children of a Sky father!"

Then she opened the box, faced it across the river. She touched what her Sky husband had told her to touch.

Across the river, the ground shook.

Across the river, a house crashed down on cowering people. And behind the house, boulders tumbled down the mountainside.

Ravens, armed and unarmed, fled in terror. And when the earth had stopped shaking, they gathered in a horrified huddle.

"Peace!" their high Chief cried out. "Peace! We

will pay reparations for what we have done to the Fireweeds."

"Peace!" Skawah echoed. But her voice was for the hovering ghosts of her murdered kinsmen. "Go in peace!" she told them.

Peace with the Ravens would come only after the reparations. After the ceremony of the white eagle feather. After the dignity of proper negotiations.

fifteen

NOW CAME THE GOLDEN AGE OF THE FIREWEEDS in the Golden Age of Temlaham. Brilliant marriages filled the houses that carried the sacred Sky emblems: Sun, Star, Rainbow, and Thunderbird. For the greatest families in the land cherished an alliance with the people whose very skin was charged with the potent symbols of Sky power.

The Fireweeds grew in pride. For were they not semidivine? Had there not been Sky power ready to save them in their hour of peril? Would there not always be Sky power ready to save them from their enemies? So who would dare to dispute *their* claim to a fishing station? Their right to a mountain hunting ground?

Though relatively few in number, they glowed with confidence. For who could stand against a people whose every possession was protected by the supernatural power of Sun, Star, Rainbow, or Thunderbird? Even the Earth spirits might be powerless against the powers of the Sky clan.

Confidence grew through two generations of peace and plenty. Some young Fireweed nobles became so braggart that they snapped their fingers at Earth spirits; they felled trees without proper ceremonial appeasement of the spirits who lived in them; they killed goats without first communing with the goats' spirit Selves. And their elders watched with consternation.

"Calamity could come, even to the Fireweeds," an old, old man reminded a group of youthful braggarts one day. But they only laughed and swaggered off.

"Who is Calamity?" a child asked the old man; and the child's eyes were as anxious as those of his three friends.

The old man led the children to the bank of the river. And there he told them the story of Prince Filthy, *The Prince Who Was Ridiculed*. He told them the story of the Raven Prince who had turned spawning salmon into living torches. And he told them of a tribe that had been almost wiped out by a volcano, after an unkindness to a frog.

The children were wide-eyed with alarm. Almost unbelieving, one of them gasped, "Those awful things happened even to the people who were wearing their Sky crests?"

"Well . . . no . . ." the storyteller confessed. "Those

things happened before there were Sky crests."

"Oh, well," the child said, much relieved.

"They could happen again," the old man snapped. "Earth spirits have great supernatural power. And our Sky ancestors knew it. Remember what the Sky Grandfather called out to Skawah's children before they left Skyland?"

"I know," a child said, very pleased that he did know. "He said, 'Do not abuse animals!' "

"I wouldn't hurt an animal," another child said. And the group agreed vigorously.

" 'Cause awful things might happen to you," one of them pointed out.

"Bah!" a hovering shaman thundered. And the children scattered like startled squirrels.

"Vengeance!" he thundered. And his eyes burned under a wild straggle of long hair.

"It's the law of life," the old man pointed out, mildly, so as not to offend anyone as awesome as a shaman.

"Is that the wisdom you have won with the years?" the shaman asked fiercely. "Is that why the Sky Grandfather's last and most important law is always forgotten when the children recount them? The law to *cherish*."

"Cherish growth," the old man remembered. But what need was there to cherish growth in a land where growth surged every springtime, as surely as the waters in the river?

"I have had many spirit visions," the shaman went on. "Many times has my soul left my body to travel into the other world." He stared across the valley as if he were seeing that spirit world now. "I have seen the spirits of the air gently shake the branches of the forest to unload their snow without damage to them. I have seen the tree spirits dancing when the birds sing. I have seen the joy of plants when they are used for healing. I have heard the happiness of the forest people when the wolves sing at mating time. Old man, is it really a fearsome world we live in? Is vengeance really the law of life?"

"Well . . . animal spirits . . ." the old man pointed out, with respectful logic. "You know what the spirits did when the boys offended the spawning salmon."

The shaman passed a weary hand across his eyes. "Fear is like a fog," he said, "blinding a man to the true way. But sleep in the sun, old man. I must prepare my son for his first spirit vision."

"Your son?" Now the old man's eyes softened with pity. For the medicine man's son had a twisted body; he could not romp with the other boys. People whispered that a rival shaman—a sorcerer—had put an evil spell on him.

The shaman murmured almost to himself. "I wish that I—alone—could prepare all the boys for their first spirit vision. My way!"

"Instead of by tribal tradition?" the old man protested, too shocked to remember that you must never risk offending a medicine man.

But the shaman was moving off.

The old man leaned back against a hummock to wonder about it. How was the shaman preparing his son? By ceremonial bathing, of course. And by fasting. And by drinking devil's club juice. Surely the shaman would warn his own son about the terrifying Beings he might have to confront all alone in the wilderness? Even the Star the boy wore might not prevail against all those powers. Even the wearer of a Sky crest should not dare to offend the Earth's spirits.

The shaman was still moving off among the trees. And he did not stop until he saw his son ahead of him. Then he slid into the shadow of a large pine tree to watch.

His son was also in the shadow of a tree, watching a group of boys who were stripping some young pine trees.

The sap was running in the trees now. And craving sweets, the boys were joyfully attacking the tender white inner bark while it was full of luscious jelly. In their excitement, they were giving one little seedling tree a very bad time. Whooping with glee, they scarcely noticed that they had fallen on it, wrestled over it, and then left it in a sad state.

But the shaman's son noticed. And after they had romped off, he hobbled up to the tiny pine tree. Kneeling awkwardly by it, he began talking to it; and as he talked he did what he could to straighten its baby trunk and firm the soil over its disturbed roots.

"You'll be all right, little friend," he kept telling it. "You'll grow tall and straight like your friends." Then his voice took on a strange intensity. "You'll grow taller and more beautiful than any of them. So . . . Grow strong, little friend! Grow tall and beautiful!"

"Cherish growth!" the shaman whispered to himself, echoing the words of the Sky Grandfather. Then he slipped away through the shadows of the pine woods. His son would need little preparation for his first spirit vision.

The village began to be very aware of the shaman's son.

"Every day he slips into the pine woods to talk to the small tree," people whispered to one another.

Then as the weeks and the months passed, an awe crept into the whispers. "The tree he talks to is outstripping its neighbors." Clearly there was magic in it. Clearly the shaman's son had uncanny spirit power. He, like his father, would be a great shaman. And they were careful to do nothing that might offend him.

Seemingly unaware of village interest, the boy continued to make the tree grow taller and more beautiful than any of its neighbors.

So, more and more, the Fireweeds kept an awed distance from their young clansman. No one dared to offend him in the slightest way. For who knew how such a powerful youth might avenge an affront?

Ravens, Wolves, and Eagles were even more careful not to offend a boy with such spirit power.

"What if he should invoke his clan's Sky spirits against us!" they whispered to one another.

sixteen

OTHER EYES, TOO, HAD BEEN WATCHING THE SHAMAN'S SON. Remote-controlled electronic eyes had been recording the strange case of accelerated growth in a young pine tree.

A film documentary had been prepared by a talented high frequency photographer, Wizl. It was titled *The Effect of Emotional Human Involvement on Plant Growth*. And Wizl was about to show it to the headquarters staff when the tragic word came from Tlu. The word was all the more tragic because a chemical compound prepared by Earth stations had accelerated plant growth in Tlu. The ETA of Doomsday had been moved twenty-seven years ahead.

But now, the signal informed them, a reaction had set in. A new blight was ravaging fields that fed the remnants of Tlu population. Dwarfed plants in the Earth Parks were dying. Doomsday was imminent. So the Earth project was canceled. Earth stations were to close up. Personnel was to return home at once to help hard-pressed experts there. And countermeasures to the lethal compound were to be formulated on the voyage home.

"After generations of effort, failure," the Project Master announced to the staff, "we are ordered home."

"Just when we may have the answer!" Wizl said, pointing to his video tape. "At least let me show it, Project Master!"

"Why not?" the PM answered, too shocked by the cancellation of his life's work to issue orders.

Numbly the staff settled back to watch the screening of *The Effect of Emotional Human Involvement on Plant Growth*. The operator readied his equipment.

"*Emotional* human involvement?" Almost automatically the Project Master challenged the title. Wizl was a superb technician, of course. But like many field workers, he had been contaminated by contact with emotional Earthmen.

The misalliance of a former top ranking rebel with a native woman had had an insidious effect. The Assistant PM, nicknamed Sunbeams, had spread contagion through the personnel. His status had saved him from elimination. But he had eventually been sent back to Tlu for the UC to deal with. The woman had been sent back to her tribe in the north. (With accouterments that would perpetuate the useful myth of Gods-from-the-Sky.) But the contagion had never been completely stamped out. It had spread especially among the young people who had been reared in Earth stations. Wizl had obviously been infected.

"Emotional human involvement, Wizl?" In a high technological society, emotion was a sickness.

"May we discuss the title after the screening, Project Master?" Wizl respectfully asked him. After the screening the PM would see where the project had gone wrong. That was Wizl's discovery, as the PM would realize. And to prepare his colleagues for this revelation, Wizl made a brief speech. He knew where *he* had gone wrong all these years, he said. He had concentrated his photography on the plants. "I should have been exploring the human factor," he told them.

The film started.

"The Effect of Emotional Human Involvement on Plant Growth," a Voice announced. The screen filled with moonlit, timbered mountains in a remote northern area of Earth.

"A stand of young pine trees in Temlaham," it continued. And the film homed in on the spot where the three boys had stripped the tender inner bark from a few trees. The stripped trunks were white in the shadowed greens of the moonlit northern pine woods.

"Now the same scene in high frequency," the voice announced. And now the scene sparkled. Trees and undergrowth were filled with radiant, flaring color. They were edged with a misty, flaring glow.

The staff sat silent. High frequency photography was nothing new. All were familiar with bioplasmic energy manifested in flaring light. And there was only mild interest in the accompanying tale of tree stripping by native boys.

"Attention to the stripped trees!" the Voice commanded. But that roused no special interest either. Naturally the injured trees showed a diminution of bioplasmic energy. Golden light faded toward the edges. The effect of blue pearls built up in the center.

"Attention to the small, trampled tree!"

Now there was a stir of interest. For the injured seedling seemed almost healthy.

"The injured seedling is receiving daily emotional attention from the shaman's son. It is receiving nothing else," the Voice continued. "It is receiving affectionate urgings to grow taller and more beautiful than the other small trees around it. And, a year later, the result of the urgings is the gossip of the village."

Now the staff was alert. For clearly the seedling had outstripped its neighbors.

"The shaman's son."

They saw the boy with the twisted body, standing before the small tree. He was fondly imploring it to grow tall and beautiful. And the scene pulled Tluan experts up in their seats. For a flaring luminosity surrounded the boy, too. A faintly visible band of bioplasmic energy flowed from the boy to the tree. It clearly increased the tree's radiance.

"Amazing," people murmured. "An input of vitality. As if the boy were a powerhouse."

"Two years later," the Voice went on. And now the once-injured seedling was the glory of its corner of the pine woods.

"The boy is avoided by the villagers. They see that he has great spirit power. They are afraid he might use that power against them."

The tape was halted briefly. Wizl made a few comments. "I have observed this phenomenon closely. And I compute that the chief factor involved in this transfer of vital energy is the high emotional charge of the human involved. I compute that it is *emotion* that makes man a powerhouse."

"Emotion?" There was embarrassment among his colleagues. These men and women had been properly insulated against emotion. It had been disciplined out of them since birth.

"Emotion . . . feeling . . . love . . . affection . . . spirit power." Wizl gave them a choice of distasteful words. "From my observations, I compute that that is what creates the mystic bond between Earthmen and plants."

"*Mystic?*" They challenged that word also.

"Next you will be filming spirit Beings," a woman called out. And laughter eased the embarrassment. Spirits had been an underground fad in Tlu at one time. But they had died for lack of proof. High frequency photography had proved the existence of a radiant bioplasmic energy in plants. But it had failed to produce a shred of evidence for misty hominoids of miniature size. The primitive concept of animism had been properly routed.

"Spirit Beings?" Wizl picked up the word. And he suggested that if Earthmen were to see the next sequence in the documentary, they would no doubt identify the radiant energy of cornstalks as the plants' spirit Selves. And they would certainly identify the flow of luminosity from the witch doctors as spirit power.

The staff watched with a new alertness as, again and again, gossamer ribbons of colored light flowed out of Earthmen into plants.

They stirred uncomfortably as later sequences showed Earth station staff members working with living plants. Here there was no talk, no excitement, no emotion. And here there was no flow of radiance.

"Here there is no feeling . . . no emotion . . . no fondness," the Voice noted. "And here there is no input of energy."

The staff made no comment. Plant experts watched the END in uncomfortable silence. Logical minds had been disturbed. Emotion was an unacceptable regression to primitive ways. Yet emotion had apparently powered that visible input of bioplasmic energy. It had given vibrant vitality to plants.

"Now!" Wizl said when the light level was raised, after the screening.

"Not now," the Project Master countered. "This station has its orders." He beckoned to several senior staff members, and led them from the room.

The others watched them go. And their shoulders slumped. "After generations of effort, failure," they muttered to one another.

"That is not so," Wizl protested. "The project is not a failure. Not when we have found the answer to our problem. Not when we have discovered that human beings can provide help to ailing plants."

All eyes turned on him.

"The documentary is amazing," men and women admitted. But Wizl's discovery was utterly at odds with established Tluan thinking.

"We have found the malfunction, have we not?" Wizl went on. "The malfunction is in *us*." There had been no flow of bioplasmic energy from Tlu experts into plants, he reminded them. Clearly, unemotional technologists did not provide the plants with a needed input of vitality.

"If we were like the savages," a woman suggested. "If we believed that plants could respond to human suggestion . . ."

"There is the probability that they can," Wizl

pointed out. The injured tree and the corn *had* responded to human urgings.

"The flow of energy was clearly a physical fact. That the flow was powered by human emotion is an acceptable probability."

"And if the concept is true?" Wizl challenged her bluntly.

"If it is true, then all Tlu is a failure."

"All Tlu *is* a failure," a silver haired man remarked. And with mechanistic efficiency he sorted through the facts. "We have promoted technological brilliance. We have inhibited emotion. Our planet is dying. Our technological brilliance can do nothing to save it. There is the probability that emotion could have saved it. So we have defeated ourselves by our own failure in information. We should long ago have uncovered this evidence that emotion works."

"So," Wizl picked up the line of logic, "our counterplan must be based on emotion. We must develop our own potential as powerhouses of vitality. On the voyage home, we must dedicate ourselves to becoming emotional about plants."

"But how does one become emotional?" an elderly woman asked. "Especially, how does one become emotional about things that are basically industrial plants housing natural machines?"

"How does one become emotional about things that mean life or death?" Wizl countered. He had been infected by long contact with emotional Earthmen.

A tall young man added his logic to the discussion. "Our ancestors had primitive visions of a land of ease and plenty, a 'Promised Land.' They achieved a Golden Age. Then something happened. There is the possibility that the outlawing of emotion lost us the 'Promised Land.' So will the highly emotional Earthmen achieve a perpetual Golden Age?"

"No," Wizl computed. "Because all their emotion is not good emotion. From my observation, there is the possibility that the emotion of hatred withers the object of the hatred and perhaps the hate as well. There is also the possibility that the emotion of fear withers the 'spirit power' of the fearful person. And fear is a big factor in Earth life. Some of that fear is due to lack of information. So I predict that Earthmen, too, will lose their 'Promised Land.' I predict that, like us, they will lose it eventually by their own failure in information."

The PM's signal light flashed. The staff rose at once.

Only Wizl stayed, briefly, to pick up his video tape.

As he laid his hand on it, a strange thing happened to him. He had a moment of blinding vision. He saw a high frequency image of Temlaham, all Temlaham. Trees and people and animals were luminous with the beautiful energy of life. And the radiance flowed out of every living thing into every other living thing. It flowed like gossamer bands of colored light, mystically binding all life into one life.

The imagine vanished.

Wizl stood stunned.

Had it been a primitive vision? Or had it been one of those visual flashes of insight that scientists claimed came to them sometimes, out of facts assembled from their unconscious? Or had it come out of the Earthmen's spirit world?

His mind still pondered the question and the wonder of the vision as he hurried to answer the PM's summons.

Then another very *un*Tluan idea struck him. Had the flash been a *sign*? Had it told him he should give a warning to the Temlahams before they, too, weakened the mystic bonds that gave vitality to all things in their world? They had some incorrect data. And one incorrect bit of data could lead to another. One initial mistake could be seriously compounded.

Wizl shook his head to clear it. In any case, it was too late now to give any warning. He would never again see Temlaham.

seventeen

THOUGH THE TEMLAHAMS HAD SEEN NO PHOTO-
GRAPHIC PROOF of a radiant energy that interpenetrated the physical bodies of all living things,
they had always felt a strong tie with the plants and
animals around them. And they still held themselves
close to a great tree to let its power flow into them.
They still ate the heart of a great beast reverently, to
let the beast's strength and speed increase their own
strength and speed. Their hunters still danced the
Wolf Dance to let that superb hunter's spirit take
possession of them for a time, to increase their own
hunting power.

Yet Wizl's moment of concern for them was well

founded. They had indeed added incorrect data to the age-old information they lived by. And their mistake was already being compounded. So perhaps they *would* lose their Promised Land, as Wizl had predicted.

The Fireweeds, especially, seemed in danger. While still recognizing their primal identity with the living things of Earth, the Fireweeds now believed they had a special, higher identity with the all-powerful Beings of the Sky. No one could equal the might they felt they had been given with their Sky crests: Sun, Star, Rainbow, and Thunderbird.

If they had known that their Sky Ancestor had not really been a Son of the Sun, but only a mortal like themselves, their arrogant nobles might not have led them into a weakening of the mystic bonds that joined them to the natural world. And the ghost of Skawah might not have haunted the proudest lodges in Temlaham.

The ghost had been glimpsed several times. It had not yet been identified. But its haunting presence was disturbing. It stirred old memories and old fears, especially among the older people, who grew ever more uneasy about the new ways they vaguely sensed all around them. The old ways were the safe ways.

From the very beginning, they remembered, the strongest of the tribe's mystic bonds had been with the cedar and the salmon.

Always they had reverenced the great cedar trees that gave them fire and houses and canoes and totem poles, as well as bark for their clothes and their household mats. Always they had rubbed their sons' flesh with living cedar boughs so that the vital power of the mighty evergreen would flow into the boys, increasing their vitality.

Always, too, they had lived with a special reverence for the Salmon People, the spirit people who lived far out in the ocean, beyond the horizon. For, year after year after year, the Salmon People had brought food to the land of the totem poles. "You are all chiefs!" they had greeted the Salmon People. And always they had been careful to return the bones to the water so that the spirit Selves of the salmon could use them again and come back to the rivers.

Because the villagers were hunters and fishermen and not planters, their strongest bonds had always been with the animal spirits who fed them. And since they had come to Temlaham, they had strengthened the bond with the mountain goats. This had been done with deeply felt rituals of gratitude and appeasement. And they had been careful to return the bones to the spirit world through ritual burning.

But now the concerned elders of the tribe sensed a dangerous weakening of that bond. They sensed a lessening of feeling for the mountain goats. Especially among the young Fireweed nobles who felt supremely confident under their Sun, Star, Rainbow, or Thunderbird.

There was no end to the peace and plenty of Temlaham. Or so it seemed. So there was no end to the arrogance of some young nobles who wore the Sky crests. And many other people, haunted by tribal memory of catastrophe, began to be uneasy.

Du'as, a boy with the Rainbow crest tattooed

across his shoulders, sensed this uneasiness in his grandfather, a famous totem pole carver. And the uneasiness crept into him, too. When he went alone into the hills to seek his spirit vision, it clouded his days; it haunted his nights when the wolves howled and the Forest People whispered among the pines and spruces.

He had been walking and fasting and praying for many days when he stood in the lengthening shadows one evening, watching a family of mountain goats.

Unaware of his presence, or else unconcerned by it, the buck—white as a ghost in the half light—grazed along a slope that led up from a cliff. Also as pale as ghosts, his family of three made its way up to him along the precipitous rock ledges below. They had just reached the top when the eagle struck. It hit the goat kid standing closest to the edge of the cliff, knocking him off.

The small body hurtled hundreds of feet down to the rocks below. And the eagle swooped down to feed on the broken body.

Du'as stood with his mouth open, aghast at what had happened. Then his quiet voice reached out to the stricken goat family. "I'm sorry," he said. "The eagle has to live. But I'm sorry. Oh, I'm sorry." And he knew his sorrow was for other goats, too, for the goats he would kill. As the eagle killed, to survive.

As if receiving the flow of feeling from the boy, the goats turned to gaze at him. And, suddenly, Du'as felt something flowing back into him from the goats. A warmth. An understanding. As clearly as if they

were speaking to him, he knew what they were telling him. He would have to kill goats, as the eagle had to kill them. They understood that. And though their physical selves would perish, their spirit Selves would never die. Their spirit Selves would find other bodies and come back to the mountains to feed the people. IF those spirit Selves had a good feeling for the people, a feeling kept strong by a flow of good feeling from the people. There was a mystic bond between hunter and hunted. And the hunter had a sacred duty to keep that bond strong.

Then, in the strange half light of the evening, in the strange hush of death, Du'as saw a radiant band of colored light vibrating between himself and the goats. He saw the same misty radiance in the trees and in the grasses. He saw it flaring and sparkling in every living thing around him. He saw it moving between things, making all things one thing.

"The spirit world!" He scarcely breathed the words.

The vision faded. And Du'as stood trembling in awe of what he had seen.

Pale as ghosts, the goats moved on up the slope. And the boy made his way back to the village. Half stunned by his spirit vision, he moved slowly through the deepening shadows on the timbered mountains.

It was very late when he finally slipped into Rainbow House. Yet people were still talking by the fire. They were talking about the ghost. Three men had glimpsed it that very night.

Still wrapped in the wonder of his own vision, Du'as held himself silent in the shadows, only half listening to them.

"It's the ghost of Skawah," one of the three was insisting. "The ghost of the young Skawah." It had clearly been the ghost of a Fireweed princess with regal ear ornaments and a white robe of weasel skins.

"But why is she haunting Temlaham?" the older people asked. And their voices sounded anxious.

"Because she is happy to see how great her descendants have become," the younger people answered.

The three men who had glimpsed her had heard a long, soft sigh. "Is a sigh the sign of a happy woman?" a grandmother challenged the young people.

"A sigh is the sign of Skawah," her granddaughter countered. "Skawah was always anxious. Perhaps she was always afraid that her children's Sky relatives would come and spirit them away to Skyland."

"She had reason for anxiety," the grandmother noted. "And perhaps she has reason for anxiety now. Perhaps she sighs over the growing brashness of the Fireweeds. Perhaps she fears for us, now."

"What is there to fear?" her granddaughter answered lightly. "In Temlaham? When we have all-powerful relatives in Skyland watching over us!"

Only vaguely disturbed by the talk, Du'as slipped silently off to his sleeping platform.

eighteen

As TIME PASSED, THE VISION FADED from the boy's mind. Yet it never quite left him.

Neither did his vague uneasiness over the growing brashness of the Temlaham people. The ghost, too, disturbed him a little. For it was glimpsed again and again.

Even on the glorious morning when Du'as was setting out on his first goat hunt, the vague uneasiness moved like a dark cloud across the brightness of the day.

Around him the village surged with excitement. Men checked on equipment. Women ducked in and out of houses. Canoes strained at their anchor stones.

Only one man stayed apart from the excitement —Du'as's grandfather, who chipped quietly away at a fragrant cedar log. Not until his grandson approached him did the old man glance up. Then he asked, "You have prepared yourself with proper fasting? And bathed, Du'as? And drunk devil's club juice?"

"Of course I have, Grandfather." What hunter would neglect the rites that nimbled his feet and strengthened his hunting power?

"And you will remember the sacred rituals when you have killed the white goats? So their ghosts will not be offended."

The boy's eyes lost their shine. His shoulders slumped a little under their Rainbow crest. For his hunting Chief, Wi-ho-om, was the most brash of all the nobles. He scorned the bone-burning rituals.

The Fireweeds, Wi-ho-om said, need not live in fear of offending Earth spirits. The Fireweeds had Sky protection. And nothing bad could happen to them. In any case, he claimed, the prehunt rituals were sufficient. There was no need for Fireweed hunters to burden themselves with tedious old ceremonies after the kill. Du'as's grandfather, he said, was old and behind the times.

Du'as's grandfather was also insistent. "You will remember the sacred rituals?"

"I . . . I will remember." And anger his Chief on his first goat hunt. And be laughed to scorn by his comrades. "I will remember," Du'as promised.

"Remember what?" another voice asked lightly. And Du'as whirled to face his hunting Chief,

Wi-ho-om, who wore the sacred Thunderbird on his chest.

"Remember what?" the prince insisted; and his dark eyes glinted with teasing. "That goats are very safe from our young Du'as?" He tossed the youth a careless grin before moving along to join his royal comrades.

"They are great hunters," Du'as said, admiring his royal clansmen.

"And foolish men," his grandfather retorted. "With no respect for lesser living creatures. Calamity will come."

The youth winced at the word *calamity*. It had become a joke among the hunters, who called Grandfather "Old Calamity" and laughed at his predictions of dire disaster.

A cedar whistle shrilled.

"Off to the hunting huts!" Wi-ho-om sang out.

Du'as sprang gratefully toward the river. The time for the hunt had come. At long last! And he would forget the vague fears that were spoiling his perfect morning.

Once across the river, packers moved out with bags and sleeping mats, with snowshoes and camp provisions. They headed up the steep slopes of Stek-yaw-den.

And there, the golden days swept by like the fleeting leaves of autumn. Du'as scaled rocky cliffs. He leaped breathless canyons. He kept watch over snares and helped older hunters corner their game.

"I'm sorry," he said silently to every goat he helped to kill. "If we didn't need the food, I wouldn't hunt you." It was not his fault, he told himself, that the older hunters did not ceremoniously pile the bones for ritual burning to return them to the spirit world. But he could not shake off his concern.

Then he snared a goat himself and killed it. "I'm sorry," he said to the ghost he knew to be hovering. "But you know we need the meat for winter." Later, he hastily gathered up the bones and took them stealthily to a cave. And there he skimped through a ritual, quickly, before someone should see him.

He noticed how often Wi-ho-om fingered his Sky charm—a bone shaped like a ceremonial club and decorated with a fantastic Sky Monster with a wolf's head and a serpentine body. Who, Wi-ho-om seemed to say, or even what, could prevail against the prince

who wore both the Thunderbird crest and the Sky Monster charm! A man so protected by Sky power need have little fear of Earth spirits.

On this hunt, Wi-ho-om left the provision bags for lesser men to fill. His goal was to prove himself master of the mountain. So, day after day, he went out after the Chief of the Goats, a magnificent buck who gave the hunters only tantalizing glimpses of a form as proud as a Thunderbird and as white as a moonlit birch tree. "I will take that goat," he vowed daily.

But all too soon the provision bags were filled to overflowing with good dried strips of meat and kidney fat. Black mounds of horns lay by the hunting huts, ready to be carved into spoons or used as grips on mountain staffs and snowshoes. Goatskins lay waiting for men to carry them down the mountain. And still the Chief of the Goats had not been taken.

"We must go home now," Du'as commented, sighing.

"Without that buck?" Wi-ho-om scoffed. "And know ourselves outsmarted by a goat? No, my young clansman, I've sworn to take that buck's head home as a trophy."

"A trophy?" Surely Wi-ho-om was joking. Of course men often treasured a trophy skin or a bear claw that had come to them after some terrible-but-needful battle; they treasured it for the power that came to them from this part of a valiant creature. But to kill a great animal just to flaunt its head as a trophy!

The age-old hunting code allowed killing for need,

126

but never killing for vanity. Du'as glanced at the provision bags and the packing boxes. There was enough meat in them for even the grimmest winter. So there must be no more killing. "The . . . the old laws of life . . ." he protested, still shocked and not quite believing.

"The laws are old," Wi-ho-om snapped. "And like old trees, they must fall and be forgotten."

"But Grandfather says—" Du'as remembered the old carver's warning. Calamity came when people grew brash, when they failed in respect for other living creatures.

"Don't think of old men's tales!" Wi-ho-om ordered. "Change with the times!"

Du'as remembered the stricken eyes of the goats on the cliff, when the eagle had knocked their little kid over. And the eagle had killed for need. He hadn't done it for vainglory. Du'as remembered his own sorrow at the need for killing. And the rush of feeling. He remembered the vision, the radiant flow of spirit power. It had been a magical moment.

"Come on, Du'as!" Wi-ho-om said briskly. "We hunt once more. And this time I will take the goats' Chief. I'll never rest if that old buck defeats me. Besides, you need the training; for I mean to make a great hunter of you."

Flattered, though very uneasy, Du'as went out along the goat trails. With other hunters he scoured rugged slopes, leaped treacherous canyons, and blocked narrow passes. Until, at last, the Chief of the Goats was cornered. Caught in a towering dead end, the mighty beast whirled to stand at bay.

"*Yi-eeee!*" Exhilarated by the chase, Du'as cried out in triumph. But, as the great beast turned to face him, as proud as a Thunderbird and as white as a moonlit birch tree, the triumph ended. Du'as opened his mouth to shout some word of protest. But a spear hurtled by him.

The great white buck fell. And Du'as, shocked by the suddenness of Death, saw again the radiance of Life. Golden light faded away toward the misty luminescence that surrounded the dying goat; and a pearly blueness spread out from the center. Then the vision faded. Only the carcass of a dead goat lay there.

Du'as could have wept, had he not been so angry. This noble beast should have died for a worthy purpose. "We don't need the meat," he burst out. And his voice rang with defiance.

"No, we don't need the meat," Wi-ho-om agreed. "So I'll take just the head to show the tribe." Careless and full of boasts, he hacked the proud head off, leaving the carcass for the wolves.

Later, he hoisted the trophy high on his spear and, swaggering, led the hunting party back across the river into the waiting village. He laughed at people who showed alarm at this disrespect to the Goat Tribe." Change with the times!" he told them.

"Calamity will come," the old carver muttered.

"To me," Du'as agreed, "for defying great Prince Wi-ho-om."

"To everybody," the old man predicted.

Showing how little he feared vengeful ghosts and Earth spirits, Wi-ho-om tossed his prized trophy to a group of highborn children. "Dance with the old goat, boys," he invited. And the children did, wearing it like a dance mask. They pulled its beard. They kicked at the boy who wore it.

A few people hid their eyes in horror. "Such ridicule!" they gasped. "Such an insult invites ghost vengeance from the Goat Tribe."

Du'as glanced back over his shoulder. But the ghost was not there. Yet he could feel the great buck's spirit Self looking down on the clowning children. Was he planning revenge on the village?

"Calamity will come," the old carver said again. "When hunting time comes again, before the time of leafing, you'll find no goats up there. Your snares will be empty, like your bellies."

nineteen

GRANDFATHER WAS WRONG, it seemed. For when the worst of the winter was over, the hunters found the customary plenty on the mountain. And every bag was filled to overflowing.

"You see?" Wi-ho-om scoffed. "The goats are powerless against my Sky power." He swelled his chest, flaunting his Thunderbird crest. Then he led his hunters on the trails again. Just for the sport of it they ranged, killing and wounding many, and leaving the carcasses for the wolves.

Du'as felt sick at heart. His ancestors had lived and died as hunters; but they had loved wild creatures. They had kept the laws of life with pride and vigor.

They had hunted as the eagle hunts, to live. And they had stayed humble before Life with rituals of gratitude and appeasement. Perhaps, Du'as thought, perhaps they, too, had had the great spirit vision.

Only necessity could excuse bloodshed. And only the knowledge that the animals' spirit Selves had not been killed could comfort the worthy hunter. So rituals of appeasement should have stayed strong and full of feeling. They should not have become a tedious mumble jumble. Du'as was suddenly ashamed of his own secret, skimpy rituals in the caves.

Then a greater shame gripped him.

Just to amuse himself, Wi-ho-om led a small hunting party to the mountain late in the springtime. Again, just for the sport of it they ranged, killing and wounding many.

Again, Du'as dared to protest.

"The laws of Life . . ." he dared to remind the others, when they finally started homeward.

". . . are old," Wi-ho-om snapped, "and like old trees they must fall and be forgotten."

But Du'as persisted. "The eagle hunts only to live," he pointed out. "The wolf hunts only to live, too. Why should we, and we alone, have sport on the mountains?"

"You're right," Wi-ho-om replied with sudden, surprising gusto. "Why should only we have sport with the mountain goats?" He swooped up a snow white goat kid from a thicket. "I'll take this to the children."

"A kid?" Du'as gasped, almost unbelieving. That was the strictest law of all, respect for the young.

131

Not caring, the prince took the goat kid home. There he flung it to the same group of highborn children. "Here, have some sport!" he urged them.

"Let's see if it can swim," a boy suggested. And he jerked a thumb toward the icy river.

Du'as walked away. He could not bear to watch. Yet he dared not protest again. So he strolled along the riverbank and finally stood watching the river's rush, his shoulders slumping under their Rainbow crest.

He was still agonizing by the river when his small sister Katla found him.

"Du'as," she panted, grabbing his fingers. "Oh, Du'as, come and stop them!" She caught her breath, then cried out with indignation, "They'll kill that baby goat if you don't stop them."

Du'as squatted down before her. He laid his hands on her heaving shoulders. "I can't help him, Katla," he grimly told her.

She shook off angry tears. "You have to stop them."

"I can't," he insisted; but he listened as she sobbed out her story.

"Oh Du'as, they . . . they threw him in the river to . . . to see if he could swim, they said. And . . . when he struggled out, they threw him in again. Then, when he got too shivery, they threw him in the fire to . . . to warm him up, they said." Her dark eyes blazed with anger. "Then, when his skin was burning, they tossed him in the river again. To cool him off, they said. He'll die. He'll die. Oh, Du'as, come and stop them!"

"I can't," her brother answered.

"Then you're not kind and brave," she stormed, whirling back toward the cruel children.

Shamed by the taunt, Du'as followed his little sister. And when he saw the kid, half-burned, half-frozen, he could stand no more. His pent-up anger burst forth. He toppled small children and sent their elders spinning.

Katla, too, moved in like an avenging whirlwind. And little princes found themselves struggling out of the icy river. Small nobles picked themselves up from startlingly hot cinders. Royal noses bled, streaming across Sky emblems.

Du'as snatched up the goat kid and ran toward his grandfather, who was waiting with ointment ready.

The old man soothed the small goat's burns with a mixture of red ocher, herbs and fish grease. Katla ran for a rabbit-skin robe to wrap around the shivering baby. Then the three of them moved off, across the river toward Stek-yaw-den.

When they had climbed high enough, and when the kid seemed strong enough, they set it down and urged it gently forward.

"Go, little friend," said Du'as. "Go, and forgive us." He glanced back over his shoulder. Again, there was no ghost there. Yet he felt the old buck's spirit Self, watching over the tiny goat kid.

"Calamity will come," warned his grandfather.

"To us," Du'as agreed. "To me especially for defying great Prince Wi-ho-om."

"To the whole village," the old man insisted darkly.

But both were wrong, it seemed. The prince said nothing, and nothing evil happened to the village. Summer and autumn and winter passed. And still nothing happened. The fish came up the river as they had always come. Lupin, daisies and paintbrush spread their lovely carpets. And berries sweetened.

"You see?" Wi-ho-om scoffed to the old carver. He patted his Sky Monster charm.

"I see. And you will see, Wi-ho-om."

"I will see you laughed at for your dismal howling. Go with the wolves, old man. And swell their nightly chorus."

"Calamity will come," the old man insisted.

The village was full of whispers.

A woman had glimpsed the ghost of Skawah.

Others claimed that the mysterious flashes and thunders on Stek-yaw-den had increased in recent moons.

"Good signs," Wi-ho-om assured fearful people. "Our Sky relatives are watching over us." Had not Thunderbirds flashed and thundered in the mountains for many moons before the Man-from-the-Sky had come down to marry Skawah and found a semidivine lineage in Temlaham?

"Good signs," the people echoed to one another. But their eyes stayed anxious.

twenty

THERE HAD INDEED BEEN FLASHES AND THUNDER above Stek-yaw-den.

Two Tlumen had managed to miss the ship home. A mysterious malfunction had developed in their transport equipment. The malfunction had not been corrected until the spaceship's departure time had passed. Then it had been corrected by Maezl with suspicious ease.

The men were Maezl and Wur, two of Wizl's crew. And the two were unlike. Alert as a stag, Maezl seemed to sniff every stray breeze that reached him. Wur was as stolidly programmed as a robot.

Maezl had been reared on Earth. He had been to

Tlu only once. And that visit had left him with no plans to go there again.

Once the possibility of going back was safely past, he had relaxed in their mountain camp some miles south of Temlaham and taken stock of their situation.

They had a good store of food tablets. They had silent weapons for securing fresh meat. They had a *Guide to Edible Earth Plants*. They had a *Guide to Earth Languages*. And they had no responsibility now to anything or anybody.

"We are freed men," Maezl had told Wur.

"What do we do with all this freedom?" Wur had asked him.

"There are several possibilities," Maezl had answered. He had sorted through them. "We could sit here until we sprout roots. We could dye ourselves and let a tribe with pretty women adopt us, as mortals. We could move in on an awed tribe as Gods-from-the-Sky. Or we could roam the hills forever, taking pictures."

"I favor the pictures," Wur had responded. He was programmed for work.

"Being Gods would be agreeable," Maezl had countered. "Still, we can always change our profession later. So now we shall take pictures."

"To whom do we show them?" Wur had reasonably asked him.

"To each other," Maezl had answered. Then he had been taken with a sudden notion. "We could develop our techniques with that remote-controlled mini-mini projector. We could hide it in the trees.

Then we could project film on pale rock face. We could make the natives think they were seeing spirit visions."

"That would be an audience," Wur had conceded. He was programmed for an audience.

Over the next few years, the project had proved interesting. While developing their techniques, they had startled many natives with "spirit visions."

Yet Maezl had grown strangely uneasy about the project. "No more spirit visions," he had told Wur.

"There is the possibility that I have had too much contact with Earthmen to want to trick them," he had told himself. For not even to himself could he admit that it was brash interference with the "spirit world" that had made him uneasy.

He had worked with Wizl on his last documentary. So he, too, questioned the established thinking of Tlumen. And when he had completed his plant photography for Wizl's documentary, he had developed an interest in wildlife photography. Over the years he had taken many shots of mountain goats on Stek-yaw-den. And while watching them by the hour to get just the right shot, he had developed what he could not yet admit was a "fondness" for mountain goats. Yet he did not mind admitting that he had developed an emotion toward the goat hunting chief, Wi-ho-om.

"If I were an Earthman," he had told Wur one day, high on Stek-yaw-den, "I would think the spirits of the mountain were planning Wi-ho-om's downfall." He had pointed to the small seismo-puter he carried.

"If you were an Earthman," Wur had pointed out,

"you would not be aware of the probability of a major seismic disturbance in the mountain." He, too, had pointed to the seismo-puter.

Maezl's eyes had widened with a sudden notion. "Perhaps we could make one more spirit vision," he had told Wur. "Perhaps we could play one last trick on ignorant Earthmen. . . . You know the tribe with the Mountain Goat totems?"

"They are stored in my memory bank," Wur had pointed out.

They were a small restless tribe of goat hunters, who roamed the hills far to the southeast of Temlaham. They roamed as if they lacked permanent hunting grounds. And they clearly felt a special bond with the goats they hunted. All their totems were Mountain Goat. Their robes were of mountain goatskins. Their dances were mountain goat dances. And their movements were strangely agile.

"If I were an Earthman," Maezl had remarked, "I would think they were human bodies possessed by goat spirits."

"If you were an Earthman," Wur had pointed out, "you would operate from incorrect information."

"It may not be as incorrect as we have been programmed to believe," Maezl had answered. "My work with Wizl convinced me that it may be Tlumen who operate from incorrect information." Then he had told Wur of his sudden notion.

They would pick out their best mountain goat shots. They would choose sequences that showed the location clearly. Then they would project their last "spirit vision" for the Mountain Goat tribe.

139

The tribe would take it as a "sign" from the Great Mountain Goat Spirit. They would add the vision to the rumors they would have heard about recent desecration of the goats on Stek-yaw-den. And they would move on to the mountain.

"And the Temlahams would massacre them," Wur had added, in logical sequence.

"Perhaps not," Maezl had countered. Yet he had no reason for that response. The idea had come to him strongly, as if—He closed his Tluan mind to the thought that it had come to him from an outraged Great Mountain Goat Spirit. He had indeed lived too long near Earthmen. He had worked too long with Wizl. He had heard too much Laetlogic in his Earth life.

"We will project this one last 'spirit vision,'" he had told Wur.

Then both men had activated their transport belts and headed south from Stek-yaw-den.

And the Temlahams had seen flashes and heard thunders on the mountain.

twenty-one

I T WAS AFTER THE MOON OF BERRIES and before the fall goat hunt that a strange thing happened. It started with the sound of cedar whistles coming on the wind from Stek-yaw-den.

"More invitations to more feasts," chirped Katla. For winter was the time of the great feasts.

"That cannot be," her grandfather objected. "The messengers have long ago brought all the invitations." His piercing eyes searched questioningly among the aspen trees that hid the approaching whistlers. "Besides, there's no tribe on Stek-yaw-den to send an invitation."

Nevertheless, four messengers appeared, coming

straight from the mountain. Their cloaks were of mountain goatskins.

"Men from Stek-yaw-den?" Du'as asked, frowning and watching closely. He felt an odd foreboding, and remembered strange tales of ancient days when animals had taken on human forms to avenge themselves on people. "Perhaps the outraged goats . . . the Great Mountain Goat Spirit . . ."

"*Pffff!*" other young people said. "Merely some new migration." Had not all the tribes arrived here by old migrations? So why not a new one? Coming from the south, perhaps, beyond-Stek-yaw-den.

"Or . . . people from the Sky?" someone dared to suggest, reminding them of the way their own ancestors' houses had been built, all in one night and one day.

"Perhaps they're just people passing through," someone else said.

In any case, Stek-yaw-den was this tribe's hunting ground.

"No doubt it's migrating people who want to stay there for at least the winter," people finally agreed. "No doubt they want to negotiate hunting rights for a brief stay in our territory." Such negotiations would take place at a feast.

Canoes were dispatched across the river to bring the four messengers to the Chief of the Sky Clan. And women hustled about, finding food for the welcome. Chiefs quickly donned regalia, picked up rattles and eagle down, the sacred pledge of peace. For negotiations must be conducted with proper ceremony. The tribe's dignity demanded it.

142

At least the messengers were equally proper in extending an invitation from their High Chief, The-Great-One-of-the-Hills. He wished to feast the people of Temlaham, at once, they said.

"Most unusual!" people whispered to one another. But all agreed that this matter must be attended to.

The Chief of the Sky Clan formally accepted the invitation. Although this was most unusual, he agreed that the people would start out the next morning.

Du'as's grandfather kept eyeing the messengers.

"Why do you look so glum?" Wi-ho-om asked him when the messengers were being taken back across the river.

"Because of what will happen up there," the carver answered. "Those men are not true men."

"How would you know?" Wi-ho-om sneered. "You see through a fog of foolish fears, old carver."

"And I see calamity," the old man answered.

"Go with the wolves!" Wi-ho-om fingered his Sky Monster charm. Nothing could harm a Sky Chief's descendant. Nothing could touch a prince protected by symbols of Sky power.

Du'as watched and listened in silence. The messengers had had strangely agile movements, he noted. Could goats still take on human form to avenge themselves on people?

When the time came to leave, at dawn the next morning, the old carver calmly started his day's work. He was not going to Stek-yaw-den. And neither was his granddaughter.

Du'as had to go. He could not be excused as too old

or too young for the journey. But he went uneasily. What if Grandfather were right? What if the outraged goat tribe *had* taken on human form to avenge the wrongs against them?

As he climbed the mountain, though, his fears lifted. For a haze was on the hills, making them deeply blue. A breeze rippled the grasses and stirred the glistening aspens. And the air was bracing.

"These are not true men?" Wi-ho-om said, nudging him as they came in sight of a house perched on a cliff. It was an ordinary big cedar house, though its totems—all Mountain Goat crests—were strange to the Temlahams.

"They must have carried their planks with them," Du'as commented. For the house had not been there before the time of leafing.

At least they were proper, formal people. They came out to meet their guests, shaking rattles, dancing, and offering food. They were proper, formal people who would negotiate correctly for hunting rights if they wished to stay here for the winter.

Yet, Du'as felt there was something missing.

All was proper inside the house, too. Drums were beating. Bright flames rose, licking toward the smoke hole. And chiefs like Wi-ho-om were properly announced and ceremoniously escorted to honored seats beyond the fire.

Du'as felt a reluctant admiration for his hunting Chief as Wi-ho-om strode arrogantly to his place. Gleaming black as wet slate, his cloak of sea otter proclaimed his ancient Coast ancestry, while the silver green pearl eyes of Thunderbird, glistening on his headdress, asserted his Sky ancestry.

Du'as himself was approached by a youth whose goatskin robe was marked by stains of red ocher. And, strangely, he sensed a flow of good feeling from his host.

"Come with me, Du'as," the stranger invited, leading his guest far to the rear of the house. "Sit here with me," he said, indicating a seat that was lost in the deepest shadow.

Dropping down on the cedar mat, Du'as found himself almost behind a projecting totem on a corner house post. "This is a poor place to see from," he thought, annoyed and puzzled. Why was he being hidden away back here? And what was it that had been missing when the hosts had danced their welcome?

Suddenly he stiffened. The eagle down! The sacred pledge of peace. That had been missing from the welcome. No one had wafted eagle down over the Temlahams. Foreboding flooded through him. Something terrible was going to happen.

The guests were all seated. And the drums began to throb faster and faster in the flickering firelight. Above the beat, a chant rose from the Mountain Goat tribe. Dancers circled the flames, wearing grotesque Goat dance masks and casting fantastic shadows.

"Their sacred tribal dance," Du'as noted with quickening interest.

It was an agile, leaping dance. At first the performers seemed to exult, like goats free on a mountain. Then, gradually, they began to creep, wary as beasts escaping from hunters.

Faces grew tense around the watching circle.

Suddenly, Du'as was afraid. There was something grim about this dancing. There was something ghostly about the Goat head dance masks. It made him shrink inside. It made his flesh crawl.

Around him the drums throbbed faster and louder, faster and louder. The chant rose higher and higher until it climaxed in a yell—a yell flung out in triumph.

"Behold our Prince!"

Another dancer leaped into the circle. Bigger than all the others, he wore a special dance mask. It was carved with a goat head, but with a single horn, placed in the center.

146

"Behold our Prince!" Again the yell of triumph.

The Prince began to dance; and where he danced, the ground began to rise.

"A trick," gasped Du'as; but his heart was pounding. Tribes had their feast house tricks, he reminded himself as the ground rose up and up until it seemed a rocky mass, a miniature mountain with a goat on top of it. For, somehow, the dancing Prince seemed to have become a living goat. He seemed to have turned into a great white buck with one horn on his forehead. And he stood defiantly, proud as a Thunderbird and as white as a moonlit birch tree.

Du'as blinked. It was a trick, he knew. A performers' trick. Yet his heart kept pounding.

"The-Great-One-of-the-Hills!" the chant proclaimed him. "When he strikes with his hooves, rocks split asunder! Rocks split like clay baked in the summer sunshine!"

Wide-eyed and trembling, the Temlahams sat, waiting.

Caught in the spell of the dance, Du'as, like the others, could move no muscle. In a strange trance, he watched The-Great-One-of-the-Hills trip down the slope, then strike his hooves against the small, magic mountain.

He felt the hard earth quake; he heard it rumble deep in the rocks beneath him; he saw the feast house collapse, with its giant timbers. People and poles and flames moved out before him. They dropped in a hideous rockslide. Screams tore the air. Boulders tumbled, crashed, and bounced off, thundering down toward the river valley.

148

Somehow, he was thrown back. And now, motion-less above it all, Du'as trembled. At last, when he could move, he grabbed for where the house post had been. But his fingers found only sharp spruce needles.

Scarcely daring to breathe on the edge of the fearful abyss, he turned to where his companion had been. But there was only a goat there, a goat whose skin showed old stains of red ocher. This was the little kid, he knew, now grown into a young goat. The stains were Grandfather's ointment.

Du'as swallowed, then glanced around in mounting wonder. For on every side were goats, leaping out of danger.

Were they his recent hosts? As in ancient days, *had* the outraged goats taken on human form to avenge the wrongs against them? Du'as trembled, clinging to the sturdy spruce branch.

Then, as clearly as if he were using words, the goat seemed to speak to him.

"Listen to me, my brother!" it seemed to say. "Listen to me, my brother! Know that the Sky Chief's Laws of Life go on forever. So does the Sky Chief's power to help his lesser creatures. This you must tell the people!"

The goat could not have spoken. Yet . . .

"How can I? . . ." He glanced down again at the crashing boulders. He dared not move an inch for fear of falling. How could he tell the people? How could he ever reach the river valley?

As if compelled by the other's gaze, Du'as turned his head to look into the goat's eyes. And it was as if strength flowed out of the goat into him.

Again, as if compelled, he took a goatskin mantle from a nearby snag and dropped it around his shoulders; he put on the matching headdress. Then, as if drawing power from the sacred regalia, he found himself suddenly confident, suddenly agile as a goat.

Wearing his One-Horned-Mountain-Goat regalia, Du'as found himself nimble and sure among the tumbling boulders. And his agile leaps soon took him down the mountain. He came home to a mourning village. For there, people who had stayed at home had now blackened their faces with ash and put on their mourning tatters. Wailing ancient clan dirges, they filled the air with sadness.

When they saw Du'as returning home from Stek-yaw-den, the old carver and Katla paddled across to meet him.

"Du'as! Du'as! Du'as!" Katla cried, flinging her arms around her beloved brother.

The carver greeted his grandson with quiet joy. Then he examined the Goat regalia.

"A great new totem has come to Temlaham," he said, running skilled fingers over the One-Horned-Mountain-Goat emblem on the headdress. "A new totem, sent by the goats who took on human form to punish a cruel people."

Du'as nodded. It must have been that. It must have been that. And so the new totem would have a humbler message than Sun, Star, Rainbow and Thunderbird. The crest and its story would remind people to cherish life all around them.

In his memory he saw an image of his old spirit

vision. And for an instant he beheld again the misty radiance in the trees, the goats, and the grasses. He saw it flaring and sparkling in every living thing. He saw it flowing between things, making all things one thing.

Then his grandfather's sigh caught his attention.

The old carver was gazing sadly across the river, at the emptied houses. He was listening to the wailing.

"Perhaps . . . perhaps we did not find Temlaham, after all," he said; and his voice was full of sorrow. "And now the dream is dead."

But was it dead?

Would the spirit world ever let the dream of a Promised Land die?

twenty-two

THE SKYMEN HAD TOUCHED TEMLAHAM LIGHTLY. Like a small comet brushing the planet Earth, they had caused only local disturbances. They had left only magical myths of the days of long ago.

The later coming of white Europeans was a greater catastrophe. Like a major cosmic accident, it caused widespread devastation. It jolted Skawah's descendants out of ancient beliefs. It shattered mystic bonds that had always joined them to the vital forces of their mountains and forests, their seas and their rivers.

More and more, their primitive awareness of the spirit world began to seem superstitious nonsense.

Their belief in their own Sky ancestry became an embarrassment to their more progressive people. Even the word Temlaham gradually vanished under a confusion of new names for old places.

Then, suddenly, in our own time, something wonderful began to happen. Starting in other parts of our planet, it reached into the Northwest. And it stirred ancient loyalties in one of Skawah's descendants, Billy Charlie, a boy of a coastal village.

There was truth in a dream that would not die, his great-grandfather had often told Billy Charlie. And always he had meant the dream of a Promised Land. But a man had to believe it, he had said. A boy had to believe it.

Billy Charlie had not believed it.

It was the dawn of a summer day. A raven called from a tall tree, as ravens had called every morning since the days of very long ago. But now there was no village to stir to its call. Now there was only the boy, Billy Charlie.

Other ravens answered from the dark forest that rose behind the arc of drift logs. Gulls wheeled and screamed above the beach. The sea mist began to stir, though there were no canoes to emerge from its ghostly shrouding. Eagle, Raven, Bear and Wolf no longer kept watch along the lonely shoreline.

The sun was coming up. At long last! And the world began to look real again to Billy Charlie. It became solid with trees and rocks, ravens and seabirds, instead of ghostly with flitting shadows and eerie, half-muffled screeches. And the sea was the sea again. So he shed his ratty old blanket and stood up to face the sunrise.

As much to do something as to warm himself, he slapped his arms around his body. Even in summer, the wind from the North Pacific was chilling. And above his jeans, his chest was bare except for the Thunderbird his great-grandfather had painted on his skin. This crazy old Indian idea was going to kill him. If the ghosts didn't get him, exposure was going to.

Ghosts?

All night he had sensed the ghosts hovering. And to get his mind off them, he made himself think of the old man's Temlaham, the Promised Land their ancestors had searched for in the days of very long ago.

"Toward the sunrise," he murmured, thinking of it still. For that was the only direction the old legend had given the band of migrant hunters, back in the beginning. Always, mystery had shrouded the Trail to Temlaham. Mystery and mists.

"Like these mists," the boy murmured. Or were they mists? he wondered, watching the vapors swirl up from the wet rocks, up toward the screams of the seabirds.

There was something there in the silence, in the writhing vapors. He could sense a presence. And his dog cowered close to him, whimpering with fear. A dog's sixth sense, he knew, was keener than man's. What did little Skook sense?

Ghosts?

No! he told himself. But . . . perhaps it was spirits, the ancient people of the forest. His people had always known there were invisible beings animating the trees. But since the coming of the white man, they had grown increasingly embarrassed by such beliefs. He himself had squirmed at mention of the other world until lately.

Billy Charlie clutched the *Harper's* magazine his teacher had given him. Mr. McKee had seemed pleased that scientists were discovering that the Indians had been right about some things.

Scientists were discovering what his people had always known—that plants *were* conscious beings. They could respond to a flow of good feeling. They could faint at a threat of harm to them. They could tune in to your very thoughts. And for Billy Charlie, that confirmation had turned the friendly old forest into a scene from Disney's *Snow White.* Now he could almost feel the branches reaching out toward him with gnarled hands and long claws, reaching out to wreak vengeance on a logging family.

He clutched his *Harper's* as if it were a club.

Spirits were for real. Now, the magazine said.

on a half-acre of soil that is mostly sand and gravel white people were *growing forty-pound cabbages and stunningly beautiful flowers by "communicating with the spirits that animate their plants."*

In midwinter! On the windblown north coast of Scotland. And who could dismiss it as "superstitious nonsense"? When a professor of agriculture had said that

the vigor, health and bloom of the plants in midwin-

ter on land which is almost barren sand cannot be explained by the application of any known cultural methods of organic husbandry.

So there were spirits, as his people had said there were. Living close to nature, they had known the truth about the world around them. Though he himself had doubted that until now.

They'd been right about the spirits. So maybe they'd been right about the ghosts, too. And maybe about the monsters also, monsters like the Wild Man of the Woods. Maybe there really was a whole scary other world of supernatural beings, the *naq noqs* of the old tribal stories. Great-grandfather had been pumping him full of the old stories, preparing him for the *old way* of getting a spirit vision.

He slipped an old bone charm out of his pocket. Shaped like a club, it had been carved to represent a monster. A fierce wolf's head trailed off into a serpent's body; and two big feathers swept back from the head, showing that this was a monster of the Air, a Sky Monster. The old man had given it to him because he had thought the charm must be a symbol of the Sky power their family had enjoyed in their Golden Days in Temlaham.

Maybe, Billy Charlie thought, maybe someone had really seen a Monster like that in the Sky. Maybe . . . He shoved it back into his pocket.

A swirl of mist rose from a log at the edge of the forest, revealing more than a log. The terrible faces of an old, old, rotting totem pole stared out at him from the living, engulfing green of the Northwest

Coast. And like a spirit leaving its dead body, the shroud of mist vanished along an opening into the deep gloom of the moss-silenced forest, toward the sunrise.

Billy Charlie caught his breath. Was that the Trail to Temlaham?

From somewhere deep in the forest came the long, high, lonely howl of a wolf. Or was it a wolf? Or some monstrous *naq noq*? Skook uttered a low growl. She bellied back from the opening in the forest wall. Was that the Trail to Temlaham? Peopled with ghosts, and guarded by monsters?

"You should not have followed me," he chided the dog in a whisper. She had found him during the night, scaring him out of his wits, then warming him with her friendly little body.

"Go home to Great-grandfather!" He held her eyes with his until she slunk off with reluctant backward glances.

"Go on!" he ordered. What he was going to do had to be done alone, as he had explained to her.

Alone now with the screaming sea birds and the silent spirits, Billy Charlie felt his eyes drawn to the old, old, rotting totem pole lying at the edge of the forest. It seemed dead. As if its ghost had indeed vanished into the forest, leaving it utterly lifeless.

Once it must have stood, tall and strong, with its back to the forest and its eyes staring out over the sea that was the very lifeblood of its people.

There had been a village here, once. So there might still be ghosts. He stared at the sea until he seemed to see ghost canoes gliding through the clean, green fringe of islands. He caught his breath. He did see them. It couldn't all be from the vagueness that came from hunger. Or could it? Or was it from the devil's club juice Great-grandfather had given him to drink?

The old man had really wanted him to do this. And he would keep the dog away until it was finished. Billy Charlie leaned his ear in the direction Great-grandfather would come from, to get the escaped dog. He had gone to a lonely place himself when he had been young, to come to terms with the other world you had to live with. He had gone to find his power. For that came to you from the spirit world, he had said. Sometimes it came to you in a spirit vision.

Billy Charlie had always scoffed at spirit visions. He had squirmed at the mention of spirit power.

Now he clutched his *Harper's* like a fetish, and the power of resurging faith in his own people's beliefs surged through him.

He was feeling queer. So he sat down to wait.

For what? Spirits? The ghosts of his ancestors? For a spirit vision? Or for a visitation from some *naq noq* more monstrous than a family ghost or a tree spirit? He glanced about him with growing apprehension. There were spirits everywhere. And they could help you or harm you. So you had to please them.

A sea gull caught his attention. It swooped to the sea and rose again with a fish.

An eagle shrieked and plummeted.

The gull dropped the fish.

The eagle caught the dropped fish before it could hit the water.

Billy Charlie's eyes shone with admiration. The swiftness of an eagle had always thrilled him. That, and the great leap of a salmon up a waterfall.

Once, the old man had said, their people had cherished a mystic bond with all the animals around them, and especially with the salmon. But now the *put-put* of an engine and the smell of the fishboat's diesel oil kept a man's mind off the spirit Selves of the salmon he was catching. Now the cutting and canning machines kept the women from their age-old salmon rituals. Now the mystic bond was broken.

The ancient mystic bond with the cedar tree, too, was broken. The scream of the power saw had little of reverence in it; and some of the older people were vaguely uneasy about the brashness of modern ways. But no one talked to the trees now before they were taken from the forest.

No one? Billy Charlie challenged his own thinking. He had seen Great-grandmother go to a spruce tree to take its roots for a needed basket. And he had heard her talk to the tree, explaining her need to its spirit Self.

"I come to beg you for this, long life-maker," she had said, "for I am going to make a basket out of you. I pray you, friend, not to feel angry with me on account of what I am going to do to you, and I beg you, friend—"

Then, Billy Charlie had slid away in shame. Talking to a tree! Now he felt a joyous surge of faith in the beliefs of his own people.

He reread a bit from the magazine. The great American plant man, Luther Burbank, had talked to the trees.

> *That plants will adapt themselves to human wishes was indicated—though generally ignored —by the experiments of Luther Burbank, the New England geneticist and experimenter with plants who gave his name to Burbank, California, where he moved at the beginning of the century to develop the pitless orange and such horticultural anomalies as an apple sweet on one side and sour on the other.*
>
> *Burbank said he was able to build plants to a form mocked up in his mind, that plants responded to his mental images, indicating some form of intelligence and transmission of thought.*
>
> *Contemplating the desert one day, Burbank*

reminded himself that every plant growing there was either bitter, poisonous, or spiny, and that each of these properties must have been developed over the course of millennia for purposes of self-defense against threatening predators. If a spiny cactus were given a human cultivator's love and protection, Burbank reasoned, it might abandon the urge to grow spines.

While conducting his experiments to make "spineless" cacti, Burbank talked to his plants to create a vibration of love. "You have nothing to fear," Burbank would tell his cacti. "You don't need your defensive thorns. I will protect you."

Gradually the plants of the desert evolved into a thornless variety.

They had done what he had asked them to do. Just as the trampled little pine tree had done what the shaman's son had asked it to do, Billy Charlie noted. He had once found the tale of the shaman's son a bit hard to swallow. But not now! There was something there, too, in that Burbank story, that applied to Temlaham, though he couldn't quite think what it was.

Somehow, he wasn't thinking very well. He was sort of fuzzy-headed. But there was something about Temlaham struggling to surface in his mind. Something about the fact that Great-grandfather wasn't sure that the tribe had found Temlaham, there, near Stek-yaw-den. He thought maybe *they* hadn't found the Promised Land, but *somebody* could find it, someday, because it was a dream that would not die.

The old man really believed the old stories. He ignored the fact that some of those punishment earthquakes could have been just plain old earthquakes in this unstable Northwest. And he had talked about Thunderbirds and the Man-from-the-Sky as if they had all been as real as Henry the Eighth or Columbus. Only more powerful.

"Sky power." There was something still struggling to surface in Billy Charlie's mind. The Fireweeds had been thankful to have Sky power because there was so much to fear out there in the other world. But maybe if they hadn't depended so much on Sky power, maybe they wouldn't have weakened the mystic bonds with the Earth around them.

A swirl of mist caught his attention. There was something there in the silence of those writhing vapors. Again he sensed a presence. Then, as he watched spellbound, the mist became luminous. It brightened into a vision of a long ago princess in a white robe of weasel skins and glistening abalone pearl ear ornaments.

"Skawah!"

He knew it was the ghost of Skawah. Yet he felt no fear of it. And she knew he felt no fear.

"We have lived too much with fear," she said to him. And her voice was a gentle, faraway sound. She spoke in the old language that his grandparents still used when they spoke together; and he understood it. "We have lived too much with fear. And fear is a fog, hiding the truth from us."

162

"But—" Their people had known the truth.

Skawah shook her head gently. They had not known the whole truth.

"They knew the truth about the spirit world," he said; and his tone fiercely defended his newly won faith in the old ways of *his people*.

"But not the truth about themselves," Skawah told him in her faraway voice. "Always they knew of the power that was out there, beyond themselves. They sought power in the Sky, in the branches of the cedar tree, in the animal dances. And there was spirit power in every living thing around them. But there was power in themselves, too. There was power for the giving, as well as for the taking. And not until men seek the spirit power in themselves will they find Temlaham."

"Temlaham? But—" The direction they had been given was "toward the sunrise."

"Toward the sunrise of a New Day," Skawah answered his thoughts.

A few lines from his *Harper's* flashed into Billy Charlie's mind, lines about the spirit gardeners on the north coast of Scotland.

Now, say the Findhorn gardeners, times are changing, a new "aquarian" age is upon us, one in which this plundered planet may yet revert to an approximation of the Biblical Garden of Eden....

"The Garden of Eden . . . the Promised Land . . . Temlaham." Billy Charlie scarcely breathed it. "That's it! That's it!" At last the thought had sur-

164

faced. Temlaham was not just a land where the rivers ran with salmon, a land where the mountain goats leaped and the eagles circled. It was a land where everyone talked to the trees, where everyone charmed the thorns off the cactus, where everyone made the desert bloom with forty-pound cabbages and stunningly beautiful flowers.

A sudden bark turned his head.

"Skook!"

She bounded toward him. Then she bellied back, whimpering with fear. The hair on her neck bristled.

The ghost! He jerked his head around to face it. But the vision of Skawah was fading. As he watched it, spellbound, it vanished in a wisp of vapor.

Skook bounded to him. She licked him with her warm tongue.

"We'll go home now," he told her, rising to his feet. "We'll go home and tell Great-grandfather that there is truth in a dream that will not die."

He felt the sun warm on his skin. And he touched the Thunderbird on his bare chest. The sign of his Sky ancestry. That, too, was a myth that would not die. And he wished he could please the old man about that, too. But even if there had been the occasional golden-haired Fireweed, as they claimed, a supernatural Sky ancestor was just too much to swallow in this Space Age.

Suddenly his eyes widened.

"Wow-woo!" he burst out. "What if—?"

What if the Man-from-the-Sky had been a SPACE-MAN?

for those who want to know more

. . . about the possibility that cosmic accidents were a worldwide source of myths.
Worlds in Collision by Dr. Immanuel Velikovsky
Doubleday & Co. Inc. and Dell Publishing Co.

. . . about the possibility that men actually did come to Earth from outer space in ancient times.
Chariots of the Gods by Erich von Daniken
We are Not the First by Andrew Tomas
G. P. Putnam's Sons and Bantam Books

. . . about the Man-from-the-Sky who did come to the Pacific Northwest, according to local legend.

The Downfall of Temlaham by Dr. Marius Barbeau
The Macmillan Company of Canada (1928)
Hurtig Publishers, Edmonton, Alberta, Canada
    (1973)
Early in this century, Dr. Barbeau collected ten versions of the Skawah legend for the National Museum of Canada. He also familiarized himself with the two versions recorded by Dr. Franz Boas and the two by Dr. Diamond Jenness before including a composite version in *The Downfall of Temlaham*. For many years available only in Northwest Collections, this book has been newly brought out by Hurtig.

. . . about plants as conscious beings.
The Secret Life of Plants by Peter Tompkins & Christopher Bird
Harper & Row
The two men who wrote the *Harper's* article that gave Billy Charlie renewed faith in the beliefs of his own people, have written a startling, fascinating account of many recent discoveries in the plant world; and they have included the Findhorn garden.

. . . about the religious beliefs of Indians of the Northwest.
The Faith of a Coast Salish Indian by Dr. Diamond Jenness
British Columbia Provincial Museum, Victoria, B.C., Canada.
Long available only in manuscript form, Dr. Jenness's memoir has been encompassed by Katzie Ethnographic Notes by Wayne Suttles, edited by Wilson Duff (1973).

167

DATE DUE 6-8

Harris, Christie
Sky man on the totem pole
X45709